Financial Records & Accounts

Workbook

NVQ Accounting Unit 5

David Cox

859969

osborne
BOOKS

Published by Osborne Books Limited
Unit 1B Everoak Estate
Bromyard Road
Worcester WR2 5HP
Tel 01905 748071
Email books@osbornebooks.co.uk
Website www.osbornebooks.co.uk

Design by Richard Holt
Cover image from Getty Images

Printed by CPI Antony Rowe Limited, Chippenham

British Library Cataloguing in Publication Data
A catalogue record for this book is available from the British Library

ISBN 978 1872962 627

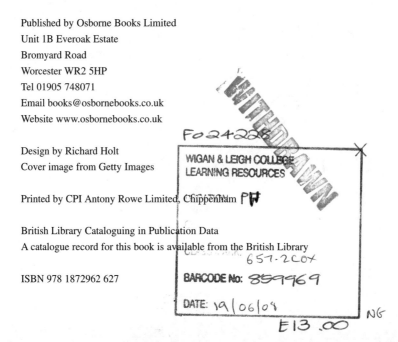

Contents

workbook activities

1	The accounting system	8
2	Double-entry book-keeping	11
3	Balancing accounts and the trial balance	15
4	Final accounts – the extended trial balance	20
5	Sole trader final accounts	24
6	Accruals and prepayments	26
7	Depreciation of fixed assets	30
8	Bad debts and provision for doubtful debts	34
9	The regulatory framework of accounting	40
10	Accounting for capital transactions	44
11	Control accounts	47
12	The journal and correction of errors	51
13	Incomplete records	54
14	Partnership final accounts	62
15	Changes in partnerships	67

simulations

1	Branson & Company	71
2	Harvey & Company	101
3	Cooper & Mason	119
4	Adcock & Tweed	141
5	Delft	161

practice examinations

1   Sarah Glass; KW Enterprise   201

2   David Nix; ABC Traders   215

3   Fresh Produce; Cookequip (AAT sample)   231

appendix

Photocopiable resources   249

About this workbook

This revised Workbook follows the order of the Tutorial text and continues to provide a wealth of practice material for students. The author has taken care to amend all the assessment material so that it accurately reflects the changes brought about by the 2003 revised Standards, using the formats and terminology that students will expect to find in their Simulations and Examinations.

Acknowledgements

The author wishes to thank the following for their help with the editing and production of the book: Jean Cox, Michael Fardon, Mike Gilbert, Rosemarie Griffiths, Claire McCarthy, Jon Moore and Derek Street. Special thanks go to Roger Petheram, Series Editor, for reading, checking and advising on the development of the text. The publisher is indebted to the Association of Accounting Technicians for its generous help and advice to the author and editor during the preparation of this text, and for permission to reproduce sample assessment material.

Author

David Cox has more than twenty years' experience teaching accountancy students over a wide range of levels. Formerly with the Management and Professional Studies Department at Worcester College of Technology, he now lectures on a freelance basis and carries out educational consultancy work in accountancy studies. He is author and joint author of a number of textbooks in the areas of accounting, finance and banking.

How to use this book

Financial Records & Accounts Workbook is designed to be used alongside Osborne Books' *Financial Records & Accounts Tutorial* and is ideal for student use in the classroom, at home and on distance learning courses. Both the *Tutorial* and the *Workbook* are designed for students preparing for assessment for Unit 5.

Financial Records & Accounts Workbook is divided into three sections: Workbook Activities, Simulations and Practice Examinations.

Workbook Activities

Workbook activities are self-contained exercises which are designed to be used to supplement the activities in the tutorial text. A number of them are more extended than the exercises in the tutorial and provide useful practice for students preparing for assessments. They have been carefully designed to reflect the style of task which students can expect to find in their assessments.

Simulations

The practice simulations in this section are designed to reflect accurately the changes brought about by the revised 2003 Standards. Simulations from the previous edition have been revised and developed to meet the requirements of the revised Standards. Osborne Books is grateful to the AAT for their kind permission to reproduce the AAT sample Simulation for the new Standards.

Practice Examinations

Osborne Books is grateful to the AAT for their kind permission to reproduce the AAT sample Examination for the new Standards and to adapt selected tasks from other assessments. These practice Examination tasks have been carefully revised to reflect the changes in the new Standards.

Answers

The answers to the tasks and exams in the *Workbook* are available in a separate *Tutor Pack*. Contact the Osborne Books Sales Office on 01905 748071 for details.

www.osbornebooks.co.uk

Visit the Osborne Books website, which contains Resources sections for tutors and students. These sections provide a wealth of free material, including downloadable documents and layouts and assistance with other areas of study.

Workbook activities

This section contains activities which are suitable for use with the individual chapters of *Financial Records & Accounts Tutorial* from Osborne Books.

Photocopiable documents you will need, such as ledger accounts, extended trial balance, trial balance, trading and profit and loss account, balance sheet, journal pages and fixed asset registers, are to be found in the Appendix at the back of this Workbook.

1 THE ACCOUNTING SYSTEM

1.1 Write out and complete the following:

(a) The .... accountant is mainly concerned with external reporting.

(b) The sales day book is an example of a book of ....

(c) Sales ledger contains the personal accounts of ....

(d) Sales account is contained in the .... ledger.

(e) Income minus .... equals ....

(f) .... minus .... equals capital.

1.2 In an accounting system, which one of the following represents the most logical sequence?

(a) book of prime entry; prime document; double-entry book-keeping; trial balance; final accounts

(b) prime document; book of prime entry; double-entry book-keeping; trial balance; final accounts

(c) prime document; book of prime entry; double-entry book-keeping; final accounts; trial balance

(d) prime document; double-entry book-keeping, book of prime entry; trial balance; final accounts

Answer (a) or (b) or (c) or (d)

1.3 Write out the figures which make up the accounting equation (assets – liabilities = capital) after each of the following consecutive transactions (ignore VAT):

- owner starts in business with capital of £10,000 comprising £9,000 in the bank and £1,000 in cash

- buys office equipment for £2,500, paying by cheque

- obtains a loan of £2,000 by cheque from a friend

- buys factory machinery for £8,000, paying by cheque

- buys office equipment for £2,000 on credit from Wyvern Office Supplies

1.4 Fill in the missing figures:

	Assets £	Liabilities £	Capital £
(a)	10,000	0	....
(b)	20,000	7,500	....
(c)	16,750	....	10,500
(d)	....	4,350	12,680
(e)	17,290	....	11,865
(f)	....	6,709	17,294

1.5   The table below sets out account balances from the books of a business. The columns (a) to (f) show the account balances resulting from a series of transactions that have taken place over time. You are to compare each set of adjacent columns, ie (a) with (b) with (c), and so on, and state, with figures, what accounting transactions have taken place in each case. (Ignore VAT).

	(a)	(b)	(c)	(d)	(e)	(f)
	£	£	£	£	£	£
Assets						
Office equipment	–	5,000	5,000	5,500	5,500	5,500
Machinery	–	–	–	–	6,000	6,000
Bank	7,000	2,000	7,000	7,000	1,000	3,000
Cash	1,000	1,000	1,000	500	500	500
Liabilities						
Loan	–	–	5,000	5,000	5,000	5,000
Capital	8,000	8,000	8,000	8,000	8,000	10,000

2 DOUBLE-ENTRY BOOK-KEEPING

Note: a set of photocopiable blank ledger accounts is printed in the Appendix.

2.1 Fill in the missing words to the following sentences:

(a) A .... entry records an account which gains value, or records an asset, or an expense.

(b) In the books of a business, the .... side of bank account records money paid out.

(c) In capital account, the initial capital contributed by the owner of the business is recorded on the .... side.

(d) Office equipment is an example of a .... asset.

(e) The purchase of a photocopier for use in the office is classed as .... expenditure.

(f) Repairs to a photocopier are classed as .... expenditure.

2.2 The following are the business transactions of Andrew King (who is not registered for VAT) for the month of October 2004:

1 Oct	Started in business with capital of £7,500 in the bank
4 Oct	Bought a machine for £4,000, paying by cheque
6 Oct	Bought office equipment for £2,250, paying by cheque
11 Oct	Paid rent £400, by cheque
12 Oct	Obtained a loan of £1,500 from a friend, Tina Richards, and paid her cheque into the bank
15 Oct	Paid wages £500, by cheque
18 Oct	Commission received £200, by cheque
20 Oct	Drawings £250, by cheque
25 Oct	Paid wages £450, by cheque

You are to:

(a) write up Andrew King's bank account

(b) complete the double-entry book-keeping transactions

2.3 Write short notes, distinguishing between:

(a) capital expenditure and revenue expenditure

(b) debit balance and credit balance

(c) bank account and cash account

(d) capital account and drawings account

2.4 The purchase of goods for resale on credit is recorded in the accounts as:

	Debit	Credit
(a)	creditor's account	purchases account
(b)	purchases account	cash account
(c)	purchases account	creditor's account
(d)	creditor's account	sales account

Answer (a) or (b) or (c) or (d)

2.5 Unsatisfactory goods, which were purchased on credit, are returned to the supplier. This is recorded in the accounts as:

	Debit	Credit
(a)	sales returns account	creditor's account
(b)	purchases returns account	creditor's account
(c)	creditor's account	purchases returns account
(d)	creditor's account	purchases account

Answer (a) or (b) or (c) or (d)

2.6 Write short notes, distinguishing between:

(a) cash purchases and credit purchases

(b) sales and sales returns

(c) carriage inwards and carriage outwards

(d) discount allowed and discount received

2.7 For each transaction below, complete the table to show the accounts which will be debited and credited:

(a)   Bought goods, paying by cheque

(b)   Cheque received for cash sales

(c)   Bought goods on credit from Teme Traders

(d)   Sold goods on credit to L Harris

(e)   Returned unsatisfactory goods to Teme Traders

(f)   L Harris returns unsatisfactory goods

(g)   Received a loan from D Perkins, by cheque

(h)   Withdrew cash from the bank for use in the business

Transaction	Account debited	Account credited
(a)		
(b)		
(c)		
(d)		
(e)		
(f)		
(g)		
(h)		

Note: ignore Value Added Tax

2.8   The following are the business transactions of Pershore Packaging for the month of January 2004:

4 Jan	Bought goods, £250, on credit from AB Supplies Limited
5 Jan	Sold goods, £195, a cheque being received
7 Jan	Sold goods, £150, cash being received
11 Jan	Received a loan of £1,000 from J Johnson by cheque
15 Jan	Paid £250 to AB Supplies Limited by cheque
18 Jan	Sold goods, £145, on credit to L Lewis
20 Jan	Bought goods, £225, paying by cheque
22 Jan	Paid wages, £125, in cash
26 Jan	Bought office equipment, £160, on credit from Mercia Office Supplies Limited
28 Jan	Received a cheque for £145 from L Lewis
29 Jan	Paid the amount owing to Mercia Office Supplies Limited by cheque

You are to record the transactions in the books of account.

Notes:

*   *Pershore Packaging is not registered for Value Added Tax*
*   *day books are not required*

2.9   Enter the following transactions into the double-entry accounts of Sonya Smith:

2004

2 Feb	Bought goods £200, on credit from G Lewis
4 Feb	Sold goods £150, on credit to L Jarvis
8 Feb	Sold goods £240, on credit to G Patel
10 Feb	Paid G Lewis the amount owing by cheque after deducting a settlement discount of 5%
12 Feb	L Jarvis pays the amount owing by cheque after deducting a settlement discount of 2%
17 Feb	Bought goods £160, on credit from G Lewis
19 Feb	G Patel pays the amount owing by cheque after deducting a settlement discount of 2.5%
24 Feb	Paid G Lewis the amount owing by cheque after deducting a settlement discount of 5%

Notes:

*   *Sonya Smith is not registered for Value Added Tax*
*   *day books are not required*

3 BALANCING ACCOUNTS AND THE TRIAL BALANCE

Note: a set of photocopiable blank ledger accounts is printed in the Appendix.

3.1 Which one of the following accounts normally has a debit balance?

(a)   loan

(b)   bank overdraft

(c)   sales

(d)   purchases

Answer (a) or (b) or (c) or (d)

3.2 Which one of the following accounts normally has a credit balance?

(a)   drawings

(b)   capital

(c)   cash

(d)   premises

Answer (a) or (b) or (c) or (d)

3.3 Produce the trial balance of Tina Wong as at 30 November 2004. She has omitted to open a capital account.

	£
Bank overdraft	1,855
Capital	?
Cash	85
Creditors	1,082
Debtors	2,115
Equipment	2,500
Purchases	2,419
Purchases returns	102
Sales	4,164
Sales returns	354
Van	7,500
Wages	1,230

3.4 The book-keeper of Lorna Fox has extracted the following list of balances as at 31 March 2004:

	£
Administration expenses	10,240
Bank overdraft	1,050
Capital	155,440
Cash	150
Creditors	10,545
Debtors	10,390
Drawings	9,450
Interest paid	2,350
Loan from bank	20,000
Machinery	40,000
Premises	125,000
Purchases	96,250
Sales	146,390
Sales returns	8,500
Telephone	3,020
Travel expenses	1,045
Value Added Tax (amount due)	1,950
Wages	28,980

You are to:

(a) Produce the trial balance at 31 March 2004.

(b) Take any three debit balances and any three credit balances and explain to someone who does not understand accounting why they are listed as such, and what this means to the business.

3.5 Fill in the missing words from the following sentences:

(a) "You made an error of .... when you debited the cost of diesel

fuel for the van to vans account."

(b) "I've had the book-keeper from D Jones Limited on the 'phone concerning the statements of

account that we sent out the other day. She says that there is a sales invoice charged that

she knows nothing about. I wonder if we have done a .... and it should

be for T Jones' account?"

(c) "There is a 'bad figure' on a purchases invoice – we have read it as £35 when it should be

£55. It has gone through our accounts wrongly so we have an error of ....

.... to put right."

(d) "Although the trial balance balanced last week, I've since found an error of £100 in the

calculation of the balance of sales account. We will need to check the other balances as I

think we may have a .... error."

(e) "Who was in charge of that trainee last week? He has entered the payment for the electricity

bill on the debit side of the bank and on the credit side of electricity – a ....

of ...."

(f) "I found this purchase invoice from last week in amongst the copy letters. As we haven't put

it through the accounts we have an error of ...."

3.6 The following are the business transactions of Mark Tansall, a retailer of computer software, for the months of January and February 2004:

Transactions for January

2004

1 Jan	Started in business with capital of £10,000 in the bank
4 Jan	Paid rent on premises £500, by cheque
5 Jan	Bought shop fittings £5,000, by cheque
7 Jan	Bought stock of software, £7,500, on credit from Tech Software
11 Jan	Software sales £2,400, paid into bank
12 Jan	Software sales £2,000, paid into bank
16 Jan	Bought software £5,000, on credit from Datasoft Limited
20 Jan	Software sales £1,500 to Wyvern School, a cheque being received
22 Jan	Software sales £2,250, paid into bank
25 Jan	Bought software from A & A Supplies £3,000, by cheque
27 Jan	Wyvern School returned software £280, cheque refund sent
29 Jan	Sold software on credit to Teme College, £2,495

Transactions for February

2004

2 Feb	Software sales £2,720, paid into bank
4 Feb	Paid rent on premises £500, by cheque
5 Feb	Bought shop fittings £1,550, by cheque
10 Feb	Software sales £3,995, paid into bank
12 Feb	Sent cheque, £7,500, to Tech Software

15 Feb	Bought software £4,510, on credit from Tech Software
19 Feb	Sent cheque, £5,000, to Datasoft Limited
22 Feb	Software sales £1,930, paid into bank
23 Feb	Teme College returned software, £145
24 Feb	Software sales £2,145, paid into bank
25 Feb	Bought software £2,120, on credit from Associated Software
26 Feb	Software sales £4,150, paid into bank

You are to:

(a) Record the January transactions in the books of account, and balance each account at 31 January 2004.

(b) Draw up a trial balance at 31 January 2004.

(c) Record the February transactions in the books of account, and balance each account at 29 February 2004.

(d) Draw up a trial balance at 29 February 2004.

Notes:

- *Mark Tansall is not registered for Value Added Tax*
- *day books are not required*
- *Mark Tansall's accounting system does not use control accounts*
- *make sure that you leave plenty of space for each account – particularly sales, purchases and bank*

4 FINAL ACCOUNTS – THE EXTENDED TRIAL BALANCE

Extended trial balance format

A blank photocopiable extended trial balance is included in the Appendix – it is advisable to enlarge it up to full A4 size. Alternatively you can set up a computer spreadsheet – but remember to allow for all the rows shown on the pro-forma – they will be needed in later Workbook Activities.

4.1 Which one of the following does not appear in the profit and loss account?

(a) closing stock

(b) purchases

(c) interest paid

(d) cash

Answer (a) or (b) or (c) or (d)

4.2 Which one of the following does not appear in the balance sheet?

(a) closing stock

(b) sales

(c) debtors

(d) bank

Answer (a) or (b) or (c) or (d)

4.3   The following trial balance has been extracted by the book-keeper of Matt Smith at 31 December 2004:

	Dr £	Cr £
Opening stock	14,350	
Purchases	114,472	
Sales		259,688
Rates	13,718	
Heating and lighting	12,540	
Wages and salaries	42,614	
Motor vehicle expenses	5,817	
Advertising	6,341	
Premises	75,000	
Office equipment	33,000	
Motor vehicles	21,500	
Debtors	23,854	
Bank	1,235	
Cash	125	
Capital		62,500
Drawings	12,358	
Loan from bank		35,000
Creditors		14,258
Value Added Tax		5,478
	376,924	376,924

Note: closing stock was valued at £16,280

You are to prepare the final accounts of Matt Smith for the year ended 31 December 2004, using the extended trial balance method.

Note: please retain the extended trial balance as it will be used on page 25 as the starting point for a further Workbook Activity.

4.4   The following trial balance has been extracted by the book-keeper of Clare Lewis at 31 December 2004:

	Dr £	Cr £
Debtors	18,600	
Creditors		11,480
Value Added Tax		1,870
Bank overdraft		4,610
Capital		25,250
Sales		144,810
Purchases	96,318	
Opening stock	16,010	
Salaries	18,465	
Heating and lighting	1,820	
Rent and rates	5,647	
Motor vehicles	9,820	
Office equipment	5,500	
Sundry expenses	845	
Motor vehicle expenses	1,684	
Drawings	13,311	
Closing stock – trading and profit & loss account		13,735
Closing stock – balance sheet	13,735	
	201,755	201,755

Tutorial note: this trial balance already incorporates the closing stock adjustments.

You are to prepare the final accounts of Clare Lewis for the year ended 31 December 2004, using the extended trial balance method.

Note: please retain the extended trial balance as it will be used on page 25 as the starting point for a further Workbook Activity.

4.5   The trial balance of Jane Richardson, who runs a secretarial agency, has been prepared at 31 December 2004 as follows:

	Dr £	Cr £
Capital		25,000
Office equipment	30,000	
Income from clients		75,450
Administration expenses	3,280	
Wages	37,145	
Rent paid	8,052	
Telephone	1,287	
Travel expenses	926	
Rates	2,355	
Debtors	3,698	
Creditors		1,074
Value Added Tax		2,021
Bank	3,971	
Cash	241	
Drawings	12,590	
	103,545	103,545

You are to prepare the final accounts of Jane Richardson for the year ended 31 December 2004, using the extended trial balance method.

Note: please retain the extended trial balance as it will be used on page 25 as the starting point for a further Workbook Activity.

5 SOLE TRADER FINAL ACCOUNTS

Conventional format

Example layouts of the trading and profit and loss account and balance sheet in conventional format – or proper form – are included in the Appendix. They may be photocopied for guidance with Workbook Activities; alternatively, a computer spreadsheet layout can be set up.

5.1 Cost of sales is calculated as:

(a) opening stock + purchases – closing stock

(b) purchases – opening stock + closing stock

(c) opening stock + purchases + closing stock

(d) purchases – opening stock – closing stock

Answer (a) or (b) or (c) or (d)

5.2 Which one of the following is used to calculate net profit?

(a) trial balance

(b) trading account

(c) balance sheet

(d) profit and loss account

Answer (a) or (b) or (c) or (d)

5.3 Which one of the following describes working capital?

(a) the excess of fixed assets over long-term liabilities

(b) the excess of current assets over long-term liabilities

(c) the excess of current assets over current liabilities

(d) the excess of fixed assets over current liabilities

Answer (a) or (b) or (c) or (d)

5.4   You are to fill in the missing figures for the following sole trader businesses:

	Sales	Opening stock	Purchases	Closing stock	Gross profit	Overheads	Net profit or loss*
	£	£	£	£	£	£	£
Business A	20,000	5,000	10,000	3,000	....	4,000	....
Business B	35,000	8,000	15,000	5,000	....	....	10,000
Business C	....	6,500	18,750	7,250	18,500	11,750	....
Business D	45,250	9,500	....	10,500	20,750	....	10,950
Business E	71,250	....	49,250	9,100	22,750	24,450	....
Business F	25,650	4,950	13,750	....	11,550	....	(3,450)

*   Note: net loss is indicated by brackets

5.5   *Please refer back to the extended trial balance of Matt Smith prepared in Workbook Activity 4.3.*

You are to prepare the final accounts of Matt Smith for the year ended 31 December 2004 in proper form, using the conventional format.

5.6   *Please refer back to the extended trial balance of Clare Lewis prepared in Workbook Activity 4.4.*

You are to prepare the final accounts of Clare Lewis for the year ended 31 December 2004 in proper form, using the conventional format.

5.7   *Please refer back to the extended trial balance of Jane Richardson prepared in Workbook Activity 4.5.*

You are to prepare the final accounts of Jane Richardson for the year ended 31 December 2004 in proper form, using the conventional format.

6 ACCRUALS AND PREPAYMENTS

Extended trial balance format

A blank photocopiable pro-forma of the extended trial balance is included in the Appendix – it is advisable to enlarge it up to full A4 size.

Conventional format

Blank photocopiable pro-formas of the trading and profit and loss account and balance sheet are included in the Appendix – it is advisable to enlarge them up to full A4 size.

6.1 Show how the following will be recorded in the accounts of a business with a financial year end of 31 December 2004.

(a) Rent paid for the business premises is £500 per month. The rental for January 2005 was paid in December 2004 and is included in the total payments during 2004 which amounted to £6,500.

(b) Motor vehicle expenses paid to 31 December 2004 amount to £8,455. On 4 January 2005 a fuel bill of £610 is received which relates to December. The bill is paid by cheque on 18 January 2005.

(c) A claim has been made on the company's insurance policy for stock damaged in a small fire. On 16 December 2004, the amount of the claim has been agreed at £180. The amount is paid by the insurance company on 26 January 2005.

(d) At 31 December 2004, the balance of telephone account is £500. Of this, £100 is the amount of personal calls made by the owner of the business.

6.2   Write short notes distinguishing between *income and expenditure accounting* and *receipts and payments accounting*.

6.3   A credit balance on accruals account indicates:

(a)   a liability and an expense owing

(b)   an asset and a prepayment of income

(c)   an asset and an accrual of income

(d)   a liability and an expense prepaid

Answer (a) or (b) or (c) or (d)

6.4   Which one of the following is a current asset?

(a)   creditors

(b)   accruals

(c)   machinery

(d)   prepayments

Answer (a) or (b) or (c) or (d)

6.5   The following trial balance has been extracted by the book-keeper of Cindy Hayward, who runs a delicatessen shop, at 30 June 2004:

	Dr	Cr
	£	£
Capital		20,932
Drawings	10,000	
Purchases	148,500	
Sales		210,900
Repairs to buildings	848	
Delivery van	5,000	
Van expenses	1,540	
Land and buildings	85,000	
Loan from bank		60,000
Bank	540	
Shop fittings	2,560	
Wages and salaries	30,280	
Discount allowed	135	
Discount received		1,319
Rates and insurance	2,690	
Debtors	3,175	
Creditors		8,295
Heating and lighting	3,164	
General expenses	4,680	
Sales returns	855	
Purchases returns		1,221
Opening stock	6,210	
Value Added Tax		2,510
Closing stock – trading and profit & loss account		7,515
Closing stock – balance sheet	7,515	
	312,692	312,692

Notes at 30 June 2004:

- rates prepaid £255
- wages owing £560
- van expenses owing £85
- goods costing £200 were taken by Cindy Hayward for her own use

You are to prepare the final accounts of Cindy Hayward for the year ended 30 June 2004:

- using the extended trial balance method
- in proper form, using the conventional format

6.6 The following list of balances has been extracted by the book-keeper of Southtown Supplies, a wholesaling business, at 31 December 2004:

	£
Opening stock	70,000
Purchases	280,000
Sales	420,000
Sales returns	6,000
Purchases returns	4,500
Discount received	750
Discount allowed	500
Electricity	13,750
Salaries	35,600
Post and packing	1,400
Premises	120,000
Fixtures and fittings	45,000
Debtors	55,000
Creditors	47,000
Bank balance	5,000
Capital	195,000
Drawings	41,000
Value Added Tax (amount due)	6,000

Notes at 31 December 2004:

- stock was valued at £60,000; this figure excludes goods which were damaged by a burst water pipe and have been scrapped (no sale proceeds); Wyvern Insurance has agreed to cover the loss of £500 incurred in writing off the goods

- electricity owing £350

- salaries prepaid £400

You are to prepare the final accounts of Southtown Supplies for the year ended 31 December 2004:

- using the extended trial balance method

- in proper form, using the conventional format

7 DEPRECIATION OF FIXED ASSETS

Extended trial balance format

A blank photocopiable pro-forma of the extended trial balance is included in the Appendix – it is advisable to enlarge it up to full A4 size.

Conventional format

Blank photocopiable pro-formas of the trading and profit and loss account and balance sheet are included in the Appendix – it is advisable to enlarge them up to full A4 size.

7.1 A car which cost £20,000 is being depreciated at 30 per cent per year using the reducing balance method. At the end of three years it will have a net book value of:

    (a)   £2,000

    (b)   £6,860

    (c)   £13,140

    (d)   £18,000

Answer (a) or (b) or (c) or (d)

7.2 A car is being depreciated using the reducing balance method. The original cost of the car was £15,000. At the end of year three it has a net book value of £5,145. What percentage of reducing balance is being used?

    (a)   20%

    (b)   25%

    (c)   30%

    (d)   35%

Answer (a) or (b) or (c) or (d)

7.3   A machine which originally cost £1,000 is sold for £350 (both amounts net of VAT). The provision for depreciation account for this machine shows a balance of £620. This means (for a VAT-registered business) that there is a:

(a)   loss on sale of £380

(b)   profit on sale of £350

(c)   loss on sale of £30

(d)   profit on sale of £30

Answer (a) or (b) or (c) or (d)

7.4   The book-keeping entries to record a profit on sale of fixed assets are:

	Debit	*Credit*
(a)	fixed asset account	profit and loss account
(b)	disposals account	profit and loss account
(c)	profit and loss account	disposals account
(d)	bank account	profit and loss account

Answer (a) or (b) or (c) or (d)

7.5   Martin Hough, sole owner of Juicyburger, a fast food shop, operating from leased premises in the town, is suspicious of his accountant, Mr S Harris, whom he claims doesn't really understand the food business. On the telephone he asks Mr Harris why depreciation is charged on a rigid formula, as surely no-one really knows how much his equipment is worth, and in fact he might not get anything for it. Draft a reply to Mr Hough from Mr Harris explaining the importance of depreciation and its application to final accounts.

7.6   Rachael Hall's financial year runs to 31 December. On 1 January 2004, her accounts show that she owns a car with an original cost of £12,000 and depreciation to date of £7,200.

On 1 October 2004, Rachael bought a new car at a cost of £15,000. She traded in the old car at a part-exchange value of £5,500 and paid the balance by cheque.

Rachael depreciates vehicles at 20 per cent per year using the straight-line method. Her accounting policy is to charge a full year's depreciation in the year of purchase, but none in the year of sale.

You are to show:

(a)   vehicles account for 2004

(b)   depreciation account for 2004

(c)   provision for depreciation account for 2004

(d)   asset disposal account for 2004

(e)   balance sheet extract at 31 December 2004

7.7 The following trial balance has been extracted by the book-keeper of Wintergreen Supplies at 31 December 2004:

	Dr	Cr
	£	£
Premises at cost	120,000	
Provision for depreciation (premises)		7,200
Long-term loan		52,800
Capital		70,000
Debtors	1,900	
Creditors		1,500
Drawings	6,750	
Cash	150	
Opening stock	4,200	
Fixtures and fittings at cost	5,000	
Provision for depreciation (fixtures and fittings)		1,000
Vehicles at cost	10,000	
Provision for depreciation (vehicles)		2,000
Bank		750
Sales		195,000
Purchases	154,000	
Wages	20,500	
Sundry expenses	9,500	
Value Added Tax		1,750
Closing stock – trading and profit & loss account		5,200
Closing stock – balance sheet	5,200	
	337,200	337,200

Notes at 31 December 2004:

- premises are to be depreciated at 2 per cent (straight-line)
- vehicles and fixtures and fittings are to be depreciated at 20 per cent (straight-line)
- wages prepaid are £560, and sundry expenses accrued are £500

You are to prepare the final accounts of Wintergreen Supplies for the year ended 31 December 2004:

- using the extended trial balance method
- in proper form, using the conventional format

7.8 Cindy Smith owns an engineering supplies business, and the following trial balance has been extracted by her book-keeper at 30 June 2004:

	Dr	Cr
	£	£
Capital		38,825
Opening stock	18,050	
Purchases	74,280	
Sales		149,410
Discounts	3,210	1,140
Rent and rates	7,280	
Returns	1,645	875
Cash	820	
Bank		13,300
Debtors and creditors	14,375	8,065
Wages and salaries	43,895	
General expenses	2,515	
Motor vehicles at cost	30,000	
Provision for depreciation on motor vehicles		7,500
Fixtures and fittings at cost	10,000	
Provision for depreciation on fixtures and fittings		3,000
Motor vehicle expenses	6,725	
Drawings	12,500	
Value Added Tax		3,180
	225,295	225,295

Notes at 30 June 2004:

- stock was valued at £20,145
- general expenses owing £175
- rates prepaid £95
- depreciate motor vehicles at 25 per cent per annum, using the reducing balance method
- depreciate fixtures and fittings at 10 per cent per annum, using the straight-line method

You are to prepare the final accounts of Cindy Smith for the year ended 30 June 2004:

- using the extended trial balance method
- in proper form, using the conventional format

8 BAD DEBTS AND PROVISION FOR DOUBTFUL DEBTS

Extended trial balance format

A blank photocopiable pro-forma of the extended trial balance is included in the Appendix – it is advisable to enlarge it up to full A4 size.

Conventional format

Blank photocopiable pro-formas of the trading and profit and loss account and balance sheet are included in the Appendix – it is advisable to enlarge them up to full A4 size.

8.1 The accounts supervisor at the firm where you work has instructed you to write off a debtor's account as bad. Which one of the following double-entry book-keeping entries will you make?

	Debit	Credit
(a)	debtor's account	bad debts written off account
(b)	bank account	debtor's account
(c)	bad debts written off account	debtor's account
(d)	debtor's account	provision for doubtful debts account

Answer (a) or (b) or (c) or (d)

Ignore VAT relief on bad debt write-off.

8.2 An increase in provision for doubtful debts will:

(a) decrease net profit for the year

(b) be recorded in the debtors' accounts

(c) decrease the cash/bank balance

(d) increase net profit for the year

Answer (a) or (b) or (c) or (d)

8.3 The profit and loss account of a business has been prepared showing a net loss of £2,350. A reduction of £150 in the provision for doubtful debts should have been made, and bad debts of £70 should have been written off. Net loss will now be:

(a) £2,130

(b) £2,270

(c) £2,430

(d) £2,570

Answer (a) or (b) or (c) or (d)

Ignore VAT relief on bad debt write-off.

8.4 You are the book-keeper at Enterprise Trading Company. The following information is available for the financial years ending 31 December 2005, 2006, 2007:

	£

- Debtor balances at 31 December 2005, before writing off bad debts — 105,200
- Bad debts written off on 31 December 2005 — 1,800
- 2.5% provision for doubtful debts created at 31 December 2005
- Debtor balances at 31 December 2006, before writing off bad debts — 115,600
- Bad debts written off on 31 December 2006 — 2,400
- 2.5% provision for doubtful debts adjusted in line with the change in the level of debtors at 31 December 2006
- Debtor balances at 31 December 2007, before writing off bad debts — 110,200
- Bad debts written off on 31 December 2007 — 1,400
- 2.5% provision for doubtful debts adjusted in line with the change in the level of debtors at 31 December 2007

Note: ignore VAT relief on bad debt write-off

You are to:

(a) write up the following accounts for 2005, 2006 and 2007 (see pages 36 and 37):

  – bad debts written off

  – provision for doubtful debts: adjustment

  – provision for doubtful debts

(b) show the effect of these transactions in the following table:

YEAR	PROFIT AND LOSS ACCOUNT				BALANCE SHEET		
	Expense		Income		Debtors	Less prov for doubtful debts	Net debtors
	Bad debts	Prov for doubtful debts	Bad debts	Prov for doubtful debts			
	£	£	£	£	£	£	£
2005							
2006							
2007							

Bad Debts Written Off Account

Dr   Cr

Date	Details	Amount	Date	Details	Amount
		£			£

Provision for Doubtful Debts: Adjustment Account

Dr   Cr

Date	Details	Amount	Date	Details	Amount
		£			£

Provision for Doubtful Debts Account

Dr   Cr

Date	Details	Amount	Date	Details	Amount
		£			£

8.5 The following trial balance has been extracted by the book-keeper of Jane Jones, who sells carpets, as at 31 December 2005:

	Dr	Cr
	£	£
Debtors	37,200	
Creditors		30,640
Value Added Tax		4,280
Bank	14,640	
Capital		50,500
Sales		289,620
Purchases	182,636	
Opening stock	32,020	
Wages and salaries	36,930	
Heat and light	3,640	
Rent and rates	11,294	
Vehicles	20,000	
Provision for depreciation on vehicles		4,000
Equipment	10,000	
Provision for depreciation on equipment		1,000
Sundry expenses	1,690	
Motor expenses	3,368	
Drawings	26,622	
	380,040	380,040

Notes at 31 December 2005:

• stock was valued at £34,000

• bad debts of £2,200 are to be written off and a provision for doubtful debts of 5% is to be created

• vehicles are to be depreciated at 20% per annum and equipment at 10% per annum (both using the reducing balance method)

• there are sundry expenses accruals of £270, and rates prepayments of £2,190

You are to prepare the final accounts of Jane Jones for the year ended 31 December 2005:

• using the extended trial balance method

• in proper form, using the conventional format

8.6 The following trial balance has been extracted by the book-keeper of Andrew Brown, a fashion designer, as at 31 December 2005:

	Dr £	Cr £
Purchases	31,480	
Sales		95,660
Opening stock	7,580	
Returns	240	620
Discounts	380	1,080
Drawings	34,720	
Premises at cost	100,000	
Provision for depreciation on premises		10,000
Fixtures and fittings	24,000	
Provision for depreciation on fixtures and fittings		3,000
Wages and salaries	18,620	
Advertising	2,260	
Rates	8,240	
Sundry expenses	7,390	
Bank	4,020	
Cash	120	
Debtors	5,000	
Bad debts written off	100	
Provision for doubtful debts		520
Creditors		3,740
Value Added Tax		3,240
Capital		81,290
Bank loan		45,000
	244,150	244,150

Notes at 31 December 2005:
- stock was valued at £6,060
- depreciate premises at 2 per cent using the straight-line method
- depreciate fixtures and fittings at 12.5 per cent per annum using the straight-line method
- provision for doubtful debts is to be 5% of debtors
- wages accrued are £500, and advertising prepaid is £350

You are to prepare the final accounts of Andrew Brown for the year ended 31 December 2005:
- using the extended trial balance method
- in proper form, using the conventional format

9 THE REGULATORY FRAMEWORK OF ACCOUNTING

9.1 (a) Explain the accounting concept of materiality.

(b) Describe three types of situation to which the concept of materiality is applicable.

(c) Suggest two problems which may occur when applying the concept of materiality.

9.2 Eveshore Electronics Limited imports electronic goods from the Far East and sells to retailers in the UK. The company has always valued its stock on the FIFO (first in, first out) basis. One of the directors comments that, because of the recent strength of the pound sterling against Far Eastern currencies, the price of imported electronic goods has been falling throughout the year. She suggests that the closing stock should be recalculated on the LIFO (last in, first out) basis.

(a) Assuming that the prices of electronic goods have been falling throughout the year, would the change suggested increase profit for the year, decrease profit, or would profit remain the same?

(b) Which accounting concept states that a business should not normally change its basis for valuing stock unless it has good reasons for so doing?

9.3 A business buys twenty units of a product in January at a cost of £3.00 each; it buys ten more in February at £3.50 each, and ten in April at £4.00 each. Eight units are sold in March, and sixteen are sold in May.

You are to calculate the value of closing stock at the end of May using:

(a) FIFO (first in, first out)

(b) LIFO (last in, first out)

(c) AVCO (average cost)

Note: where appropriate, work to the nearest penny.

9.4 Wyvern Office Supplies sells a range of pens, paper, computer supplies and other office sundries. One of its lines is photocopying paper for which the stock movements in January 2004 were:

1 January	Stock of 800 reams (a ream is 500 sheets) of photocopying paper brought forward at a cost of £2.00 per ream
5 January	Sold 700 reams
11 January	Bought 1,200 reams at £2.20 per ream
15 January	Sold 600 reams
19 January	Bought 1,000 reams at £2.10 per ream
21 January	Sold 400 reams
26 January	Bought 700 reams at £2.25 per ream

The selling price of each ream is £3.25.

You are to calculate the value of:

(a) sales for January

(b) the closing stock at 31 January and cost of sales for January, assuming that stock is valued on the FIFO (first in, first out) basis

(c) the closing stock at 31 January and cost of sales for January, assuming that stock is valued on the LIFO (last in, first out) basis

9.5 YZ Limited is formed on 1 January 2004 and trades in two products, Y and Z. At the end of its first half-year the stock movements of the two products are as follows:

2004	PRODUCT Y		PRODUCT Z	
	Bought (units)	Sold (units)	Bought (units)	Sold (units)
January	100 at £4.00		200 at £10.00	
February		80 at £10.00	100 at £9.50	
March	140 at £4.20			240 at £16.00
April	100 at £3.80		100 at £10.50	
May		140 at £10.00	140 at £10.00	
June	80 at £4.50			100 at £16.00

The company values stock on the FIFO (first in, first out) basis.

At 30 June 2004, the net realisable value of each type of stock is:

product Y   £1,750.00

product Z   £1,950.00

£3,700.00

You are to calculate the value of:

(a)   total sales for the half-year

(b)   the closing stock at 30 June 2004 for each product using the FIFO basis

(c)   the total at which the company's stocks should be valued on 30 June 2004 in order to comply with standard accounting practice

(d)   cost of sales for the half-year in order to comply with standard accounting practice

9.6 Which one of the following is revenue expenditure?

(a)   purchase of a computer for the office

(b)   legal costs for the purchase of property

(c)   cost of extension to property

(d)   quarterly electricity bill

Answer (a) or (b) or (c) or (d)

9.7   Which one of the following is capital expenditure?

(a)   repairs to motor vehicles

(b)   goods taken by owner for own use

(c)   cost of raw materials used in extending the premises

(d)   renewing the electrical wiring in the office

Answer (a) or (b) or (c) or (d)

9.8   Wages paid to own employees who have redecorated the office are:

(a)   capital expenditure

(b)   debited to profit and loss account

(d)   debited to premises account

(d)   credited to profit and loss account

Answer (a) or (b) or (c) or (d)

9.9   Classify the following costs (tick the appropriate column):

	capital expenditure	revenue expenditure
(a) purchase of motor vehicles		
(b) depreciation of motor vehicles		
(c) rent paid on premises		
(d) wages and salaries		
(e) legal fees relating to the purchase of property		
(f) re-decoration of office		
(g) installation of air-conditioning in office		
(h) wages of own employees used to build extension to the stockroom		
(i) installation and setting up of a new machine		

10 ACCOUNTING FOR CAPITAL TRANSACTIONS

10.1 Which one of the following is an intangible fixed asset?

(a) vehicles

(b) goodwill

(c) hire purchase

(d) premises

Answer (a) or (b) or (c) or (d)

10.2 Eveshore Enterprises is considering the use of hire purchase as a means of financing a new computer. Which of the following statements is correct?

(a) at the end of the hire purchase contract, ownership of the computer will pass from the finance company to Eveshore Enterprises

(b) a hire purchase contract is the same as an operating lease

(c) at the end of the hire purchase contract, the finance company will collect the computer from Eveshore Enterprises

(d) as the computer is being financed through hire purchase, it is not recorded on the balance sheet of Eveshore Enterprises

Answer (a) or (b) or (c) or (d)

10.3 (a) An extract from the fixed asset register of Mereford Manufacturing is shown on the next page. You are to update the register with depreciation on the fixed asset for the years ended 31 December 2002 and 2003.

(b) The fixed asset is sold on 20 April 2004 for £600 (net of VAT). The company does not charge depreciation in the year of sale. You are to complete the fixed asset register showing the machine's disposal.

EXTRACT FROM FIXED ASSET REGISTER

Description/serial no	Date acquired	Original cost £	Depreciation £	NBV £	Funding method	Disposal proceeds £	Disposal date
Machinery							
Moulding machine	7/2/00	10,000.00			Cash		
Year ended 31/12/00			2,000.00	8,000.00			
Year ended 31/12/01			2,000.00	6,000.00			

10.4 Perham Publishing, which has a financial year end of 31 December, bought a colour laser printer on 11 February 2002 at a cost of £2,000 (paid by cheque). The printer is expected to last for four years, after which its estimated value will be £260. Depreciation is charged at 40 per cent each year using the reducing balance method; it is charged in full in the year of purchase, but not in the year of sale.

The printer is part-exchanged for a more up-to-date model on 19 October 2004. The part-exchange allowance is £400.

You are to

(a) show the accounting entries (journal and cash book not required) to record the acquisition, depreciation and disposal of the printer for the years 2002, 2003, 2004.

Note: VAT is to be ignored

(b) draw up a page from the fixed asset register to show the printer's acquisition, depreciation and disposal. (A photocopiable page from the fixed asset register is provided in the Appendix).

10.5 John and Sara Smith run a delivery company called 'J & S Transport'. They started in business on 1 January 2002 with two vans which cost £16,000 each (paid by cheque). On 1 January 2004, a further two vans were bought at a cost of £18,000 each (paid by cheque) and, on 20 March 2004, one of the original vans was sold for £8,000 (cheque received).

Depreciation is charged at 25 per cent each year using the reducing balance method; depreciation is charged in the year of purchase, but none in the year of sale.

The Smith's financial year end is 31 December.

You are to show the accounting entries (journal and cash book not required) to record the acquisition, depreciation and disposal of vans for the years 2002, 2003 and 2004.

Notes:

• VAT is to be ignored

• use one fixed asset account for all vans, one depreciation account and one provision for depreciation account

10.6 (a) Write short notes, distinguishing between:

• an operating lease

• a finance lease

(b) Explain the accounting treatment of each of these types of lease in the accounts of the lessee (the person to whom the asset is leased).

11 CONTROL ACCOUNTS

11.1 Would the following errors cause a difference between the balance of the sales ledger control account and the total of the balances in the sales ledger?

(a) The sales returns day book was undercast by £100.

(b) The amount of a credit note issued was credited to the account of Martley Traders instead of Martley Manufacturing.

11.2 On 31 December 2004 the balances of the creditor accounts in the subsidiary (purchases) ledger of Thomas Limited were listed, totalled, and compared with the balance of the purchases ledger control account. The total of the list of creditor balances amounted to £55,946. Investigations were carried out and the following errors were discovered:

(a) a creditor balance of £553 had been listed as £535

(b) settlement discount received of £100 had been credited to the creditor's account

(c) a credit note received for £141 (including VAT) had not been recorded in the creditor's account

(d) a creditor balance of £225 had been listed twice

You are to record the appropriate adjustments in the table below; show clearly the amount involved and whether it is to be added or subtracted.

		£
Total of list of creditor balances		55,946
Adjustment for (a)	add/subtract	....
Adjustment for (b)	add/subtract	....
Adjustment for (c)	add/subtract	....
Adjustment for (d)	add/subtract	....
Revised total to agree with purchases ledger control account		....

11.3   The following accounts, together with their balances at 1 January 2004, form the subsidiary (purchases) ledger of A Austin:

B Bedford   £596.41

C Chrysler   £602.03

D De Lorean   £228.14

F Ford   £487.29

During January the following transactions took place:

5 Jan   Bought goods on credit from C Chrysler £127.55 and from F Ford £298.31

7 Jan   Bought goods on credit from B Bedford £348.19 and from D De Lorean £422.19

11 Jan   Returned goods to C Chrysler £12.34 and to B Bedford £59.68

15 Jan   Paid D De Lorean £250.00 on account, by cheque

21 Jan   Paid F Ford by cheque the balance owing on the account after deducting a 5% settlement discount

You are to:

(a)   write up the accounts in the subsidiary (purchases) ledger of A Austin for January 2004, balancing them at the end of the month

(b)   prepare a purchases ledger control account for January 2004, balancing it at the end of the month

(c)   reconcile the control account balance with the subsidiary accounts at 1 January and 31 January 2004

Note: VAT is to be ignored on all transactions and day books are not required.

11.4   The purchases ledger of Rowcester Traders contains the following accounts on 1 February 2004:

Arley Supplies Limited, balance £1,549.81 credit

Balfour Brothers, balance £39.20 debit

W James & Company, balance £598.27 credit

Mereford Manufacturing Company, balance £495.83 credit

Northern Equipment Limited, balance £727.86 credit

W Williams, balance £1,040.40 credit

The following transactions took place during February:

3 Feb   Bought goods on credit from Arley Supplies Limited, £986.28, and from Balfour Brothers £1,167.24

6 Feb   Paid W Williams a cheque for the balance of the account after deducting 2.5% settlement discount

10 Feb   Bought goods on credit from W James & Company £452.13, and from W Williams £1,595.26

11 Feb   Paid Northern Equipment Limited a cheque for the balance of the account

16 Feb   Returned goods to Arley Supplies Limited for £236.09

17 Feb   Paid Arley Supplies a cheque for the balance of the account, after deducting 2.5% settlement discount

18 Feb   Returned goods to Northern Equipment Limited for £97.39

24 Feb   Paid W James & Company the amount owing by cheque, after deducting 2.5% settlement discount

26 Feb   Bought goods on credit from Arley Supplies Limited £699.84

29 Feb   Transfer of debit balance of £364.68 in the sales ledger to Mereford Manufacturing Company's account in the purchases ledger

You are to:

(a)   write up the accounts in the subsidiary (purchases) ledger of Rowcester Traders for February 2004, balancing them at the end of the month

(b)   prepare a purchases ledger control account for February 2004, balancing it at the end of the month

(c)   reconcile the control account balance with the subsidiary accounts at 1 February and 29 February 2004

Note: VAT is to be ignored on all transactions and day books are not required.

11.5   Prepare purchases ledger control and sales ledger control accounts for the month-ended 31 January 2004 from the following information:

Balances at 1 January 2004

* debtors, £35,563 debit

* creditors, £24,080 credit

Totals for the month from the day books

* sales day book, £205,610

* purchases day book, £137,825

* sales returns day book, £3,081

* purchases returns day book, £1,843

Totals for the month from the cash book

- settlement discount allowed, £548
- payments received from debtors, £197,045
- settlement discount received, £494
- payments made to creditors, £135,048
- debtors' cheques returned unpaid, £856

Other transactions

- set-off entries between sales ledger and purchases ledger, £812
- bad debts written off, £110
- increase in provision for doubtful debts, £250

11.6   You are an accounts assistant at Martinez and Company, a business which imports children's toys and sells them to retailers. The accounts supervisor asks you to review the closing stock of goods for resale at 30 April 2004 (the end of the company's financial year).

The computerised stock records show a stock valuation at cost of £83,290. This figure has been debited to stock control account by the computer and posted to the trading and profit and loss account for the year. However, some stock items have been reduced in price at the year end. The details are shown below:

Stock code	Quantity in stock 30 April 2004	Cost £	Normal selling price £	Reduced selling price £
DC 57	100	5.00	9.00	4.00
JC 55	75	24.00	33.50	22.00
AC 28	220	12.00	19.50	14.00

You are to:

(a)   calculate the adjustments to be made to the stock valuation at 30 April 2004

(b)   prepare a journal entry for authorisation by the accounts supervisor to adjust the stock valuation

(c)   show how the authorised adjustment will be recorded in stock control account

12 THE JOURNAL AND CORRECTION OF ERRORS

For journal entries involving sales ledger and purchases ledger, it is to be assumed that control accounts are incorporated into the double-entry book-keeping system and that the accounts for debtors and creditors are kept in subsidiary ledgers.

Note: a photocopiable blank journal page is printed in the Appendix.

12.1 Which one of the following will not be recorded in the journal?

(a) opening transaction of a new business

(b) goods taken by the owner for her own use

(c) closing stock valuation at the year end

(d) petty cash payment for office window cleaning

Answer (a) or (b) or (c) or (d)

12.2 The purchase of stationery, £25, has been debited in error to office equipment account. Which one of the following journal entries will correct the error?

	Debit		*Credit*	
(a)	Office equipment	£25	Stationery	£25
(b)	Suspense	£25	Office equipment	£25
(c)	Stationery	£25	Office equipment	£25
(d)	Stationery	£25	Suspense	£25

Note: VAT is to be ignored

Answer (a) or (b) or (c) or (d)

12.3 A trial balance fails to agree by £27 and the difference is placed to a suspense account. Later it is found that a payment for postages of £63 has been entered in the accounts as £36. Which one of the following journal entries will correct the error?

	Debit		*Credit*	
(a)	Suspense	£36	Postages	£36
	Postages	£63	Suspense	£63
(b)	Suspense	£27	Postages	£27
(c)	Postages	£27	Bank	£27
(d)	Postages	£36	Suspense	£36
	Suspense	£63	Postages	£63

Answer (a) or (b) or (c) or (d)

12.4 What is the effect on the previously-calculated profit and the balance sheet of each of the following?

(a) sales account has been overcast by £1,000

(b) closing stock has been undervalued by £250

(c) telephone expenses account has been undercast by £100

(d) discount received of £135 has been omitted

(e) depreciation of the vehicles of £1,250 for the year has not been made

(f) a reduction of £100 in provision for bad debts has not been made

(g) bad debts totalling £75 have not been written off

12.5 You have recently taken over writing up the double-entry accounts of Manston Sales Limited. You have found a number of errors made by the previous book-keeper as follows:

(a) credit sale of goods for £250 to Didsbury Limited has not been entered in the accounts

(b) a cheque for £195 paid to William Thomas, a creditor, has been debited to the account of another creditor, Thomas Williams

(c) office stationery costing £50 has been debited to office equipment account

(d) a credit purchase of goods for £167 from A Carver has been entered in the accounts as £176

(e) purchases returns account has been undercast by £100 as has electricity account

You are to take each error in turn and:

• state the type of error

• show the correcting journal entry

Note: VAT is to be ignored.

12.6 Dave James is the book-keeper for Western Traders Limited. At 30 June 2005 he is unable to balance the trial balance. The difference, £86 credit, is placed to a suspense account in the main ledger pending further investigation.

The following errors are later found:

(a) sales account is overcast by £100

(b) a payment cheque for postages, £65, has been recorded in postages account as £56

(c) commission received of £150 has been debited to both the commission received account and the bank account

(d) stationery expenses of £105, paid by cheque, have not been entered in the expenses account

You are to:

• make journal entries to correct the errors

• show the suspense account after the errors have been corrected

Note: VAT is to be ignored

12.7 Show the journal entries for the following transfers which relate to Jim Hoddle's business for the year ended 30 June 2005:

(a) the balance of sales account, £125,000, is to be transferred to trading and profit and loss account

(b) the balance of purchases account, £78,500, is to be transferred to trading and profit and loss account

(c) closing stock is to be recorded in the accounts at a valuation of £15,500

(d) postages account has a balance of £1,800, but the franking machine meter shows that there is £200 unused; the amount due for the year is to be transferred to profit and loss account

(e) salaries and wages account has a balance of £45,500, but £1,500 is owing; the amount due for the year is to be transferred to profit and loss account

(f) depreciation on vehicles for the year is calculated at £3,000

(g) bad debts written off account has a balance of £180; the amount is to be transferred to profit and loss account

(h) the provision for doubtful debts is £250; the amount is to be increased to £300

13 INCOMPLETE RECORDS

13.1 James Hendry owns a business which sells office stationery. Most of his customers are firms in the area, to whom he sells on credit terms. Although he does not keep a full set of accounting records, the following information is available in respect of the year ended 31 December 2005:

Summary of assets and liabilities:

	1 Jan 2005	31 Dec 2005
	£	£
Shop fittings (cost £10,000)	8,000	7,000
Stock	25,600	29,800
Bank balance	4,000	8,000
Cash	1,000	1,600
Debtors	29,200	20,400
Creditors	20,800	16,000
Accrual: business expenses	–	500

Summary of the business bank account for the year ended 31 December 2005:

	£
Receipts from customers	127,800
Payments to suppliers	82,600
Drawings	20,000
Business expenses	20,600

Other information

Shop fittings are being depreciated at 10% per year, using the straight-line method.

You are to:

(a) calculate the amount of sales during the year

(b) calculate the amount of purchases during the year

(c) calculate the figure for business expenses to be shown in the profit and loss account for the year ended 31 December 2005

(d) prepare James Hendry's trading and profit and loss account for the year ended 31 December 2005

(e) prepare James Hendry's balance sheet as at 31 December 2005

Note: VAT is to be ignored on all transactions

13.2 You are preparing the 2004 accounts of Heidi Johnson, who runs a mobile carpet and curtain cleaning business. Heidi keeps few accounting records, but the person who prepared the accounts last year has left a set of working accounts with start of year balances. The balances have been entered in the accounts.

From Heidi's business bank statements you have prepared the following summary for the year ended 31 December 2004:

	£	£
Opening balance		1,547
Receipts:		
Cash takings	2,150	
Receipts from debtors	55,290	
Inheritance	12,000	69,440
		70,987
Payments:		
Payments to creditors	18,450	
Drawings	20,000	
Vehicle expenses	4,250	
General expenses	4,100	
Assistant's wages	9,200	
Purchase of new van on 1 July 2004	13,500	69,500
Closing balance		1,487

The following information is available:

- At 31 December 2004, vehicle expenses were prepaid by £210.
- At 31 December 2004, assistant's wages of £480 were owing.
- At 31 December 2004, debtors were £6,410; creditors were £2,890.
- Invoices to customers during the year totalled £61,450.
- Heidi thinks that debtors amounting to £460 will not pay, and should be written off as bad debts.
- Some customers pay by cheque, while others pay in cash. Heidi has kept no records of the cash received but knows that she paid general expenses of £220 in cash; the rest she kept as drawings. At 31 December 2004, she had a cash float of £125.
- The inheritance was received from the estate of her grandmother: the amount was paid into the business bank account to help finance the new van. (She will keep her old van in order to provide flexibility when she and her assistant are working on different sites.)
- Heidi depreciates vans, using the straight-line method, on the basis of a five-year life from the date of acquisition, with a nil residual value.
- At 31 December 2004 there was a stock of cleaning materials valued at £1,430.

You are to reconstruct the ledger accounts for the year ended 31 December 2004, showing the balances carried forward at the end of the year and/or the amounts to be transferred to profit and loss account. Ledger accounts with appropriate balances are set out on pages 56 to 61.

Notes:

- dates are not required
- the following accounts are not supplied and do not need to be shown:
  - profit and loss
  - sales
  - purchases
  - capital
- VAT is to be ignored on all transactions

Dr		**Bank Account**		Cr
Details	Amount	Details		Amount
	£			£
Balance b/d	1,547			

Dr		**Cash Account**		Cr
Details	Amount	Details		Amount
	£			£
Balance b/d	86			

Dr   **Vehicle Expenses Account**   Cr

Details	Amount	Details	Amount
	£		£
		Balance b/d	105

Dr   **Prepayments Account**   Cr

Details	Amount	Details	Amount
	£		£

Dr   **Van Account**   Cr

Details	Amount	Details	Amount
	£		£
Balance b/d	10,000		

Dr   **Depreciation Account**   Cr

Details	Amount	Details	Amount
	£		£

Dr   **Provision for Depreciation Account – Vans**   Cr

Details	Amount	Details	Amount
	£	Balance b/d	£ 6,000

Dr   **General Expenses Account**   Cr

Details	Amount	Details	Amount
	£		£
Balance b/d	110		

Dr   **Assistant's Wages Account**   Cr

Details	Amount	Details	Amount
	£		£

Dr   **Accruals Account**   Cr

Details	Amount	Details	Amount
	£		£

Dr   **Debtor's Account**   Cr

Details	Amount	Details	Amount
	£		£
Balance b/d	4,120		

Dr   **Creditor's Account**   Cr

Details	Amount	Details	Amount
	£	Balance b/d	£ 2,250

Dr   **Drawings Account**   Cr

Details	Amount	Details	Amount
	£		£

Dr   **Materials Used Account**   Cr

Details	Amount	Details	Amount
Balance b/d (opening stock)	£ 1,050		£

Dr		**Bad Debts Written Off Account**	Cr
Details	Amount	Details	Amount
	£		£

13.3 The following figures are extracted from the accounts of Wyvern Systems Limited for the year ended 30 June 2005:

* sales for the year, £300,000

* opening stock, £20,000

* closing stock, £40,000

* purchases for the year, £260,000

You are to calculate:

(a) cost of sales for the year

(b) gross profit for the year

(c) gross profit percentage mark up

(d) gross profit percentage margin

13.4 Talib Zabbar owns a shop selling children's clothes. He is convinced that one of his employees is stealing goods from the shop. He asks you to calculate from the accounting records the value of stock stolen.

The following information is available:

* sales for the year, £160,000

* opening stock at the beginning of the year, £30,500

* purchases for the year, £89,500

* closing stock at the end of the year, £21,500

* the gross profit margin achieved on all sales is 40 per cent

You are to calculate the value of stock stolen (if any) during the year.

14 PARTNERSHIP FINAL ACCOUNTS

14.1 A partnership may choose to over-ride some or all of the accounting rules in the Partnership Act 1890 by the partners entering into a separate:

(a)   appropriation account

(b)   accounting policy

(c)   partnership agreement

(d)   loan agreement

Answer (a) or (b) or (c) or (d)

14.2 Profits of a two-person partnership are £32,800 before the following are taken into account:

- interest on partners' capital accounts, £1,800
- salary of one partner, £10,000

If the remaining profits are shared equally, how much will each partner receive?

(a)   £10,500

(b)   £11,400

(c)   £12,300

(d)   £16,400

Answer (a) or (b) or (c) or (d)

14.3 Mike and Bernie are in partnership as 'M & B Builders'. The following figures are extracted from their accounts for the year ended 31 December 2004:

	£	
Capital accounts at 1 January 2004:		
Mike	30,000	Cr
Bernie	20,000	Cr
Current accounts at 1 January 2004:		
Mike	1,560	Cr
Bernie	420	Dr
Drawings for the year:		
Mike	21,750	
Bernie	17,350	
Partnership salary:		
Bernie	7,500	
Interest on capital for the year:		
Mike	1,500	
Bernie	1,000	
Share of profits for the year:		
Mike	20,200	
Bernie	10,100	

You are to show the partners' capital and current accounts for the year ended 31 December 2004.

14.4   Clark and Pearce are in partnership selling business computer systems. The following trial balance has been taken from their accounts for the year ended 30 June 2004, after the calculation of gross profit:

	Dr £	Cr £
Gross profit		105,000
Salaries	30,400	
Electricity	2,420	
Telephone	3,110	
Rent and rates	10,000	
Discount allowed	140	
Office expenses	10,610	
*Closing stock	41,570	
Debtors and creditors	20,000	6,950
Value Added Tax		5,240
Bad debts written off	1,200	
Provision for doubtful debts		780
Office equipment at cost	52,000	
Provision for depreciation on office equipment		20,800
Clark: Capital account		60,000
Current account		430
Drawings	20,600	
Pearce: Capital account		30,000
Current account		300
Drawings	15,700	
Bank	21,750	
	229,500	229,500

*   Only the closing stock is included in the trial balance because gross profit for the year has been calculated already.

Notes at 30 June 2004:

- depreciate the office equipment at 20 per cent, using the straight-line method
- Pearce is to receive a partnership salary of £12,000
- remaining profits and losses are shared as follows: Clark two-thirds, Pearce one-third

You are to:

(a)   prepare the partnership final accounts for the year ended 30 June 2004, using the extended trial balance method

(b)   show the partners' capital and current accounts for the year

(c)   prepare the partnership final accounts for the year ended 30 June 2004 in proper form, using the conventional format

14.5 Sara and Simon Penny are in partnership running a catering service called 'Class Caterers'. The following trial balance has been taken from their accounts for the year ended 31 March 2005:

	Dr £	Cr £
Capital accounts:		
Sara		10,000
Simon		6,000
Current accounts:		
Sara		560
Simon		1,050
Drawings:		
Sara	12,700	
Simon	7,400	
Purchases	11,300	
Sales		44,080
Opening stock	2,850	
Wages	8,020	
Rent and rates	4,090	
Sundry expenses	1,390	
Equipment	8,000	
Debtors	4,500	
Creditors		5,850
Value Added Tax		1,350
Bank	8,640	
	68,890	68,890

Notes at 31 March 2005:

• stock was valued at £3,460

• sundry expenses owing, £110

• depreciation is to be charged on the equipment at 10 per cent per year

• Sara is to receive a partnership salary of £8,000

• interest is to be allowed on partners' capital accounts at 10 per cent per year

• remaining profits and losses are to be shared equally

You are to:

(a) prepare the partnership final accounts for the year ended 31 March 2005, using the extended trial balance method

(b) show the partners' capital and current accounts for the year

(c) prepare the partnership final accounts for the year ended 31 March 2005 in proper form, using the conventional format

14.6 Anne Adams and Jenny Beeson are partners in an electrical supplies shop called 'A & B Electrics'. The following trial balance has been taken from their accounts for the year ended 30 June 2005:

		Dr	Cr
		£	£
Capital accounts:	A Adams		30,000
	J Beeson		20,000
Current accounts:	A Adams		780
	J Beeson		920
Drawings:	A Adams	16,000	
	J Beeson	10,000	
Opening stock		26,550	
Purchases and sales		175,290	250,140
Returns		1,360	850
Rent and rates		8,420	
Wages		28,700	
Motor vehicle expenses		2,470	
General expenses		6,210	
Motor vehicle at cost		12,000	
Fixtures and fittings at cost		4,000	
Provision for depreciation:	motor vehicle		3,000
	fixtures and fittings		800
Debtors and creditors		6,850	12,360
Value Added Tax			2,410
Bank		22,009	
Cash		1,376	
Bad debts written off		175	
Provision for doubtful debts			150
		321,410	321,410

Notes at 30 June 2005:
- stock is valued at £27,750
- rates paid in advance £250
- wages owing £320
- provision for doubtful debts to be equal to 2 per cent debtors
- depreciation on fixtures and fittings to be provided at 10 per cent per year using the straight line method
- depreciation on motor vehicles to be provided at 25 per cent per year using the reducing balance method
- Anne Adams is to receive a partnership salary of £6,000
- remaining profits and losses are to be shared equally

You are to:

(a) prepare the partnership final accounts for the year ended 30 June 2005, using the extended trial balance method

(b) show the partners' capital and current accounts for the year

(c) prepare the partnership final accounts for the year ended 30 June 2005 in proper form, using the conventional format

15 CHANGES IN PARTNERSHIPS

15.1 Mia, Nell and Olly are in partnership sharing profits equally. Mia is to retire and it is agreed that goodwill is worth £30,000. After Mia's retirement, Nell and Olly will continue to run the partnership and will share profits equally. What will be the goodwill adjustments to Nell's capital account?

(a)   debit £10,000,   credit £10,000

(b)   debit £10,000,   credit £15,000

(c)   debit £15,000,   credit £15,000

(d)   debit £15,000,   credit £10,000

Answer (a) or (b) or (c) or (d)

15.2 Norman and Oliver are in partnership sharing profits equally. Each has a capital account with a balance of £75,000. Peter joins as a new partner introducing £80,000 capital. The new profit share will be Norman (2), Oliver (2) and Peter (1). An adjustment is made for goodwill on the admission of Peter to the value of £40,000, but no goodwill is to be left in the accounts. What will be the balance of Oliver's capital account after the creation and write off of goodwill?

(a)   £71,000

(b)   £79,000

(c)   £91,000

(d)   £95,000

Answer (a) or (b) or (c) or (d)

15.3 The partnership of Fame, Fortune and Fear has asked you to assist its book-keeper in the finalisation of its accounts for the year ended 31 March 2005.

The following information is available:

- The net profit of the business for the year is £152,000, before taking into account any appropriations.

- The original partners of the business are Fame and Fortune. They shared profits on an equal basis until 1 April 2004 when Fear then joined them. Fear agreed to introduce £60,000 by cheque on admission to the business. It was then agreed that the new profit sharing ratio would be:

Fame	3/8
Fortune	3/8
Fear	2/8

- On 1 April 2004 goodwill was valued at £80,000. No adjustment was made for goodwill at that time, but it is now the wish of the partners that goodwill is introduced against their opening capital accounts. (No goodwill account is to be maintained in the accounts of the partnership).

- Partnership salaries for the year to 31 March 2005 are as follows:

	£
Fame	20,000
Fortune	20,000
Fear	30,000

- All partners receive interest of 10 per cent per annum on the year end balance of their capital accounts.

- The credit balances on capital and current accounts as at 1 April 2004 were as follows:

	Capital Accounts	Current Accounts
	£	£
Fame	110,000	6,500
Fortune	90,000	7,800

- Partners' drawings were as follows:

	£
Fame	28,000
Fortune	32,000
Fear	36,000

Task 1

Prepare the partners' capital accounts for the year ended 31 March 2005, recording all the necessary entries for the admission of Fear to the partnership.

Task 2

Prepare the partnership appropriation account for the year ended 31 March 2005.

Task 3

Prepare the partners' current accounts for the year ended 31 March 2005.

15.4   Henry, Ian and Jenny are in partnership sharing profits equally. Ian retired on 31 December 2004. The balance sheet drawn up immediately before Ian's retirement was as follows:

	£	£
Fixed assets		120,000
Current assets		55,000
Bank		15,000
		190,000
Current liabilities		50,000
		140,000
Capital Accounts:		
Henry	42,000	
Ian	43,000	
Jenny	50,000	
		135,000
Current Accounts:		
Henry	4,000	
Ian	(2,000)	
Jenny	3,000	
		5,000
		140,000

Upon Ian's retirement from the partnership:

- goodwill was agreed to be worth £36,000

- his current account balance was to be transferred to his capital account

- he was to be paid £10,000 of his capital and share of the goodwill by cheque, and the balance was to be left as a loan to the partnership

- Henry and Jenny were to continue in partnership sharing profits and losses equally

- No goodwill is to remain in the accounts

Task 1

You are to prepare the partners' capital accounts, showing the retirement of Ian.

Task 2

You are to show the balance sheet immediately after Ian's retirement from the partnership.

15.5 Nisha and Dil are in partnership. Net profit for the year ended 30 June 2005 is £36,400 before appropriation of profit. Their capital account balances at 30 June 2005 are Nisha £25,000, Dil £20,000. Their partnership agreement allows for the following:

- partnership salaries
  - Nisha £8,000
  - Dil £12,000
- interest is allowed on capital at 4 per cent per year on the balance at the year end
- profit share, effective until 31 December 2004
  - Nisha 50%
  - Dil 50%
- profit share, effective from 1 January 2005
  - Nisha 60%
  - Dil 40%

Notes:

- no accounting entries for goodwill are to be recorded
- profits accrued evenly during the year
- drawings for the year were: Nisha £15,200, Dil £22,100

Task 1

Prepare the appropriation account for the partnership of Nisha and Dil for the year ended 30 June 2005.

Task 2

Update the current accounts for the partnership for the year ended 30 June 2005. Show clearly the balances carried down.

Dr				**Partners' Current Accounts**			Cr
2004/05		Nisha	Dil	2004/05		Nisha	Dil
		£	£			£	£
1 Jul	Balance b/d	650	–	1 Jul	Balance b/d	–	1,950

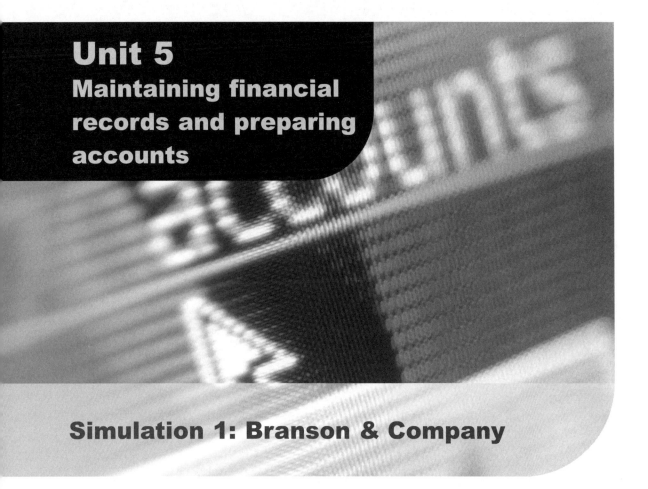

Unit 5
Maintaining financial records and preparing accounts

Simulation 1: Branson & Company

NVQ Element coverage

5.1 maintaining records relating to capital acquisition and disposal

5.2 collecting and collating information for the preparation of final accounts

5.3 preparing the final accounts of sole traders and partnerships

Scenario and contents

This Simulation is based on Branson & Company, a business which sells office supplies to business customers in its area. The tasks include:

- recording the purchase and disposal of a company car
- updating the fixed asset register
- postings to the main ledger
- correction of errors and making year end adjustments
- correction of errors, including the use of suspense account
- stock valuation and reconciliation
- extended trial balance
- the preparation of a partnership appropriation account and balance sheet

Suggested time allocation: four hours

SIMULATION 1
BRANSON & COMPANY

SITUATION

Your name is Val Denning and you are an accounts assistant working for Branson & Company, a partnership business owned by two partners, Amy Brandreth and Sanjay Sondin. You report to the firm's accountant, Jenny Holden.

Branson is a business that buys office stationery in bulk from manufacturers. The products are then sold in smaller quantities to business customers in the area. The company employs sales representatives who keep in contact with existing customers and develop new sales leads. Branson's business premises consist of a warehouse and packing department, and a showroom and office.

This Simulation relates to Branson's accounting year ended 31 March 2004. Today's date is 20 April 2004.

Books and records

Branson maintains a full main ledger with manual ledger accounts in alphabetical order. Money coming in and going out is recorded in a manual cash book which serves both as a book of prime entry and as a ledger account.

Branson also maintains a manual fixed asset register. This includes details of capital expenditure (but not revenue expenditure) incurred in acquiring fixed assets, as well as details of depreciation and disposals.

Stock records of the various products bought and sold by Branson & Company are kept using a computerised system.

Accounting policies and procedures

Branson is registered for VAT and all of its sales are standard-rated.

Branson classifies its fixed assets into three categories: company cars, warehouse equipment, and other fixed assets. For each category the main (general) ledger includes accounts relating to cost, depreciation charge (ie the profit and loss expense), accumulated depreciation (ie the balance sheet provision), and disposals.

Company cars are depreciated at a rate of 45% per annum on the reducing balance. Warehouse equipment and other fixed assets are depreciated at 25% per annum straight-line, assuming nil residual value. In the year of an asset's acquisition a full year's depreciation is charged, regardless of the exact date of acquisition. In the year of an asset's disposal, no depreciation is charged. Company car running costs are recorded in the firm's accounts as an administration overhead. Branson is not able to recover input VAT on the purchase of company cars. Similarly, the firm is not required to account for output VAT when company cars are disposed of.

Authorisation for the acquisition and disposal of fixed assets, and for the method of finance derives from the partners and is communicated to you by means of a memorandum from the firm's accountant at the beginning of each month in which an acquisition or disposal is planned. In the month of March 2004 one acquisition and one disposal took place; these are referred to in the memorandum on page 76.

The Simulation

In this Simulation you will be required to perform a number of tasks leading up to the preparation of an extended trial balance and partnership appropriation account for the year ended 31 March 2004, together with a balance sheet at that date.

TASKS

This Simulation is designed to let you show your ability to maintain financial records and prepare accounts.

You should read the whole Simulation before you start work, so that you are fully aware of what you will have to do. The answer pages are on pages 82 to 100.

The Simulation is divided into two parts and 12 tasks as follows:

PART ONE

Accounting for fixed assets

Ledger accounting and the trial balance

You should spend about two hours on this part

Task 1

Refer to the memorandum on page 76 and the supplier's invoice on page 77. This refers to the purchase of a new company car and the trade-in of an existing company car. You are required to record the acquisition and the trade-in in the fixed asset register (see pages 83 to 84) and in the main ledger (which starts on page 85).

Notes:

• A creditor's account has been opened in the name of the supplier of the car, Hylex Motors, in the subsidiary (purchases) ledger.

• You are not required to show the journal entries for these transactions.

• You are reminded that Branson is not able to recover VAT on the acquisition of company cars.

Task 2

By reference to the fixed asset register (see pages 82 to 84), you are required to calculate the depreciation for the year on each of the company cars and also on each item of warehouse equipment. You should record the relevant amounts in the fixed asset register and in the main (general) ledger (which starts on page 85). You should also calculate the depreciation for the year on 'other fixed assets' and record the relevant amount in the main ledger. Note: you are not required to show the journal entries for these transactions.

Task 3

A member of staff has listed the company cars actually present on Branson's premises at the close of business on 31 March 2004. His list is on page 78. You are required to compare this list with the details recorded in the fixed asset register and to describe any discrepancies in a memorandum to the firm's accountant. Use the memorandum form on page 94.

Task 4

The main (general) ledger already includes sales and purchases transactions up to 29 February 2004. The sales and purchases day books have been totalled for March 2004 and the totals are displayed on page 78. You are required to post these totals to the main (general) ledger. Note that the invoice from Task 1 has not been included in the March totals because it was not received until 1 April.

Task 5

Refer to the business cash book on page 79. You are required to post from the cash book to the main (general) ledger for the month of March 2004.

Task 6

You are required to bring down a balance as at 1 April 2004 on each account in the main ledger, including suspense account, (pages 85 to 93) and to enter the balances in the first two money columns of the trial balance (page 96). Note: there is no need to balance accounts which have only one transaction.

Total the two columns of the trial balance. They should be equal; if they are not, check your work to find and correct the difference.

PART TWO

Adjusting and extending the trial balance

Drafting final accounts

You should spend about two hours on this part

Task 7

The debit entry in the suspense account (£750) represents a cheque made out on the business bank account earlier in the year. The payee is not known to you as a supplier or employee of Branson & Company. You are required to describe how you would ascertain the nature of this payment so that you can account for it correctly. Set out your answer on page 95.

Note: once you have completed this task you should ask your assessor to explain what the payment represents. You will need this information to complete Task 8.

Task 8

The credit entry on the suspense account is the proceeds on disposal of a fixed asset included in the category 'other fixed assets'. No other entries have been made in the main (nominal) ledger in respect of this disposal. The asset originally cost £2,317.69, and its accumulated depreciation at 31 March 2003 was £946.23. You are required to draft journal entries dated 31 March 2004, to clear the balance on the suspense account. Set out your entries, with full narrative, on page 95. Note: you are not required to adjust your answer to Task 2 in the light of this transaction.

Task 9

Details of Branson's closing stocks are given in the memorandum on page 80. You are required to calculate the value of the closing stock at 31 March 2004 for inclusion in the trial balance. Set out your answer on page 98. Note: you are not required to show the journal entry for any stock adjustment you might make.

Task 10

On the trial balance you are required to make appropriate adjustments in respect of the following matters:

*   Journal entries prepared in Task 8

*   Closing stock calculated in Task 9

*   Accruals and prepayments. For details of these see page 80.

Task 11

You are required to extend the trial balance (pages 96 to 97). This includes totalling all columns of the trial balance and making entries to record the net profit or loss for the year ended 31 March 2004 and the figures for the balance sheet at that date.

Task 12

Details of the partnership agreement between Amy Brandreth and Sanjay Sondin are given on page 81.

(a)   Using the figure for net profit or loss from the extended trial balance, you are to prepare the appropriation account for the partnership for the year ended 31 March 2004. Set out your answer on page 99.

Note: you should work to the nearest £.

(b)   Update the current accounts for the partnership for the year ended 31 March 2004, showing clearly the balances carried down. Set out your answer on page 99. Remember to pick up any transactions from earlier Tasks which affect the partners' current accounts.

Note: you should work to the nearest £.

(c)   From the extended trial balance prepare a balance sheet for the partnership as at 31 March 2004, showing clearly the total net assets. Set out your answer on page 100.

Note: you should work to the nearest £.

You are not required to record any transactions on ledger accounts in respect of this Task.

DATA FOR TASK 1

MEMORANDUM

To: Val Denning

From: Jenny Holden

Subject: Fixed asset acquisitions/disposals in March 2004

Date: 2 March 2004

Only one fixed asset acquisition is planned for the month of March. Our salesman, Andy Noble, will trade in his old car (registration W104 PTY) and purchase a new one. The new one will be financed partly by the trade-in value (agreed at £1,850), and partly by cash.

DATA FOR TASK 1

SALES INVOICE

HYLEX MOTORS

45 Extines Road, Blankton
Telephone: 01489 22514 Fax: 01489 56178
VAT registration: GB 318 1627 66

Date/tax point   27 March 2004

Invoice no   42176

Invoice to:

Branson & Co
Unit 6 Chalmers Trading Estate
Blankton
BT3 4NY

Registration: VX04 TMS   Registration date: 27/3/04   Stock number: Q4510
Chassis no: TWQQAW 66780   Engine no: ER43218   Sales person: Mary Easton

	£
Ford Mondeo	10,900.00
VAT at 17.5%	1,907.50
	12,807.50
Vehicle excise duty (12 months)	165.00
Total due	12,972.50
Less: part-exchange (W104 PTY)	1,850.00
Balance to pay	11,122.50

Terms: net, 30 days

DATA FOR TASK 3

COMPANY CARS ON THE PREMISES, 31 MARCH 2004

Y321 HDR - in car park;   X33 FGY - in car park;   VX04 TMS - in car park

DATA FOR TASK 4

Sales day book totals, March 2004	£
Total value of invoices	36,514.59
Sales value	31,076.25
VAT	5,438.34
Purchases day book totals, March 2004	£
Total value of invoices	9,133.18
Administration overheads	991.24
Purchases	4,871.22
Selling and distribution overheads	524.87
Warehouse overheads	1,451.09
VAT	1,294.76

DATA FOR TASK 5

CASHBOOK — CB122

Receipts Total £	Sales ledger control £	Other £	Date 2004	Details	Cheque no	Total £	Purchases ledger control £	Other £
5,034.72			1 Mar	Balance b/f				
4,265.77	4,265.77		6 Mar	Cash and cheques banked				
5,931.20	5,931.20		13 Mar	Cash and cheques banked				
3,773.81	3,773.81		20 Mar	Cash and cheques banked				
6,071.88	6,071.88		27 Mar	Cash and cheques banked				
5,512.67	5,512.67		31 Mar	Cash and cheques banked				
			3 Mar	Hanway plc	19331	1,192.45	1,192.45	
			5 Mar	Peters Limited	19332	365.11	365.11	
			9 Mar	Wright & Parkin	19333	2,651.08	2,651.08	
			16 Mar	Westcott Limited	19334	3,006.12	3,006.12	
			17 Mar	Sidlow & Morris	19335	299.52	299.52	
			24 Mar	Harper John & Co	19336	2,561.29	2,561.29	
			24 Mar	Paul Darby plc	19337	278.01	278.01	
			27 Mar	Brandreth: drawings	19338	500.00		500.00
			27 Mar	Sondin: drawings	19339	450.00		450.00
			31 Mar	Wages and salaries (see analysis below)	19340	10,480.05		10,480.05
			31 Mar	Balance c/d		8,806.42		
30,590.05	25,555.33					30,590.05	10,353.58	11,430.05
8,806.42			1 Apr	Balance b/d				
				Wages and salaries analysis				
				Admin overhead				3,120.42
				Sell and dist overhead				3,427.88
				Warehouse overhead				3,931.75
								10,480.05

DATA FOR TASK 9

MEMORANDUM

To: Val Denning

From: Jenny Holden

Subject: Stock valuation

Date: 10 April 2004

The closing stock valuation taken from the computer records shows a figure of £16,221.35 at 31 March 2004.

However, some items have been reduced in price after the financial year end. The details are as follows:

Stock code	Quantity in stock 31 March 2004	Cost £	Normal selling price £	Reduced selling price £
TBL	150	20.00	35.00	22.50
LAS	200	15.00	25.00	10.00
IJT	50	10.00	17.50	9.50

DATA FOR TASK 10

Accruals and prepayments at 31 March 2004

Branson & Company does not attempt to calculate accruals and prepayments for non material amounts, defined as being anything less than £200.

The only two items which may amount to more than this are included in administration overheads, as follows:

- Office rental of £3,250 was paid in December 2003 in respect of the six months ending 30 June 2004.

- Telephone and fax charges amount to about £630 per quarter. At 31 March 2004 these charges had already been paid for the quarter ended 31 January 2004, but the invoice for the subsequent quarter is not expected to arrive until May 2004.

Data For Task 12

Partnership Agreement

The partnership agreement allows for the following:

Partners' salaries

–	Brandreth	£10,000
–	Sondin	£8,000

Interest on capital

    –   5% per annum on the balance at the year end

Profit share

–	Brandreth	one-half
–	Sondin	one-half

ANSWER PAGES

Tasks 1 and 2

EXTRACT FROM FIXED ASSET REGISTER

Description/serial no	Location	Date acquired	Original cost £	Depreciation £	NBV £	Funding method	Disposal proceeds £	Disposal date
Warehouse equipment								
Packing machine 45217809	Warehouse	20/6/00	3,456.08			Cash		
Year ended 31/3/01				864.02	2,592.06			
Year ended 31/3/02				864.02	1,728.04			
Year ended 31/3/03				864.02	864.02			
Fork lift 299088071	Warehouse	12/6/01	4,008.24			Cash		
Year ended 31/3/02				1,002.06	3,006.18			
Year ended 31/3/03				1,002.06	2,004.12			
Bar coder 51123412	Warehouse	12/2/02	582.44			Cash plus		
Year ended 31/3/02				145.61	436.83	trade in		
Year ended 31/3/03				145.61	291.22			

Tasks 1 and 2, continued

EXTRACT FROM FIXED ASSET REGISTER

Description/serial no	Location	Date acquired	Original cost £	Depreciation £	NBV £	Funding method	Disposal proceeds £	Disposal date
Company cars								
W412 RTW	Car park	25/8/00	8,923.71			Cash		
Year ended 31/3/01				4,015.67	4,908.04			
Year ended 31/3/02				2,208.62	2,699.42			
Year ended 31/3/03				1,214.74	1,484.68			
W104 PTY	Car park	15/3/01	8,643.00			Cash		
Year ended 31/3/01				3,889.35	4,753.65			
Year ended 31/3/02				2,139.14	2,614.51			
Year ended 31/3/03				1,176.53	1,437.98			

Tasks 1 and 2, continued

EXTRACT FROM FIXED ASSET REGISTER

Description/serial no	Location	Date acquired	Original cost £	Depreciation £	NBV £	Funding method	Disposal proceeds £	Disposal date
Company cars								
X33 FGY	Car park	18/9/01	10,065.34			Cash plus		
Year ended 31/3/02				4,529.40	5,535.94	trade in		
Year ended 31/3/03				2,491.17	3,044.77			
Y321 HDR	Car park	13/12/02	9,460.26			Cash		
Year ended 31/3/03				4,257.12	5,203.14			

Tasks 1, 2, 4, 5 and 6

MAIN LEDGER

Administration overheads

Date 2004	Details	Amount £	Date 2004	Details	Amount £
1 Mar	Balance b/f	15,071.23			

Brandreth: capital account

Date 2004	Details	Amount £	Date 2004	Details	Amount £
			1 Mar	Balance b/f	17,063.24

Brandreth: current account

Date 2004	Details	Amount £	Date 2004	Details	Amount £
1 Mar	Balance b/f	11,056.73			

Tasks 1, 2, 4, 5 and 6

MAIN LEDGER

Company cars: cost

Date 2004	Details	Amount £	Date 2004	Details	Amount £
1 Mar	Balance b/f	37,092.31			

Company cars: depreciation charge

Date 2004	Details	Amount £	Date 2004	Details	Amount £

Company cars: accumulated depreciation

Date 2003	Details	Amount £	Date 2003	Details	Amount £
			1 Apr	Balance b/f	25,921.74

Tasks 1, 2, 4, 5 and 6

MAIN LEDGER

Company cars: disposals

Date 2004	Details	Amount £	Date 2004	Details	Amount £

Other fixed assets: cost

Date 2004	Details	Amount £	Date 2004	Details	Amount £
1 Mar	Balance b/f	18,923.50			

Other fixed assets: depreciation charge

Date 2004	Details	Amount £	Date 2004	Details	Amount £

Tasks 1, 2, 4, 5 and 6

MAIN LEDGER

Other fixed assets: accumulated depreciation

Date 2003	Details	Amount £	Date 2003	Details	Amount £
			1 Apr	Balance b/f	6,224.12

Other fixed assets: disposals

Date 2004	Details	Amount £	Date 2004	Details	Amount £

Purchases

Date 2004	Details	Amount £	Date 2004	Details	Amount £
1 Mar	Balance b/f	125,133.09			

Tasks 1, 2, 4, 5 and 6

MAIN LEDGER

Purchases ledger control

Date 2004	Details	Amount £	Date 2004	Details	Amount £
			1 Mar	Balance b/f	18,457.20

Sales

Date 2004	Details	Amount £	Date 2004	Details	Amount £
			1 Mar	Balance b/f	225,091.42

Sales ledger control

Date 2004	Details	Amount £	Date 2004	Details	Amount £
1 Mar	Balance b/f	24,617.03			

Tasks 1, 2, 4, 5 and 6

MAIN LEDGER

Selling and distribution overhead

Date 2004	Details	Amount £	Date 2004	Details	Amount £
1 Mar	Balance b/f	14,303.12			

Sondin: capital account

Date 2004	Details	Amount £	Date 2004	Details	Amount £
			1 Mar	Balance b/f	8,703.28

Sondin: current account

Date 2004	Details	Amount £	Date 2004	Details	Amount £
1 Mar	Balance b/f	12,912.29			

Tasks 1, 2, 4, 5 and 6

MAIN LEDGER

Stock

Date	Details	Amount	Date	Details	Amount
2003		£	2003		£
1 Apr	Balance b/f	12,513.77			

Suspense

Date	Details	Amount	Date	Details	Amount
2004		£	2004		£
26 Jan	Bank	750.00	24 Feb	Bank	1,124.55

VAT

Date	Details	Amount	Date	Details	Amount
2004		£	2004		£
			1 Mar	Balance b/f	5,091.27

Tasks 1, 2, 4, 5 and 6

MAIN LEDGER

Warehouse equipment: cost

Date	Details	Amount	Date	Details	Amount
2004		£	2004		£
1 Mar	Balance b/f	8,046.76			

Warehouse equipment: depreciation charge

Date	Details	Amount	Date	Details	Amount
2004		£	2004		£

Warehouse equipment: accumulated depreciation

Date	Details	Amount	Date	Details	Amount
2003		£	2003		£
			1 Apr	Balance b/f	4,887.40

Tasks 1, 2, 4, 5 and 6

MAIN LEDGER

Warehouse equipment: disposals

Date 2004	Details	Amount £	Date 2004	Details	Amount £

Warehouse overheads

Date 2004	Details	Amount £	Date 2004	Details	Amount £
1 Mar	Balance b/f	27,109.67			

Task 3

MEMO
To: **From:**   **Subject:**   Check on company cars at 31 March 2004   **Date:**

Task 7

Payment of £750

Task 8

Journal				
Date	Details		Dr	Cr
2004			£	£

Tasks 6, 10 and 11:   **Extended Trial Balance**

account name	ledger balances	
	Dr	Cr
	£	£
Administration overheads		
Brandreth: capital account		
Brandreth: current account		
Company cars: cost		
Company cars: depreciation charge		
Company cars; accumulated depreciation		
Company cars: disposals		
Other fixed assets: cost		
Other fixed assets: depreciation charge		
Other fixed assets: accumulated depreciation		
Other fixed assets: disposals		
Purchases		
Purchases ledger control		
Sales		
Sales ledger control		
Selling and distribution overheads		
Sondin: capital account		
Sondin: current account		
Stock		
Suspense		
VAT		
Warehouse equipment: cost		
Warehouse equipment: depreciation charge		
Warehouse equipment: accumulated depreciation		
Warehouse equipment: disposals		
Warehouse overheads		
Bank		
Total		

name __**BRANSON & COMPANY**__   date __**31 MARCH 2004**__

adjustments		profit and loss		balance sheet	
Dr £	Cr £	Dr £	Cr £	Dr £	Cr £

Task 9

Stock valuation at 31 March 2004

....

....

....

....

....

....

....

....

....

....

....

....

....

....

....

....

....

....

....

....

....

....

Task 12(a)

BRANSON & COMPANY

Appropriation account for the year ended 31 March 2004

	£	£
Net profit from extended trial balance		
Salaries:		
Brandreth		
Sondin		
Interest on capital:		
Brandreth		
Sondin		
Balance of net profit		
Share of profit:		
Brandreth		
Sondin		

Task 12(b)

CURRENT ACCOUNTS

		Brandreth £	Sondin £			Brandreth £	Sondin £
2004				2004			
1 Mar	Balances b/f	11,057	12,912				

Task 12(c)

BRANSON & COMPANY

Balance sheet at 31 March 2004

	£	£
Fixed assets:		
Company cars		
Other fixed assets		
Warehouse equipment		
Current assets:		
Stock		
Debtors		
Bank		
Prepayments		
Current liabilities:		
Creditors		
VAT		
Accruals		
Net current assets		
Total net assets		
Capital accounts:		
Brandreth		
Sondin		
Current accounts:		
Brandreth		
Sondin		

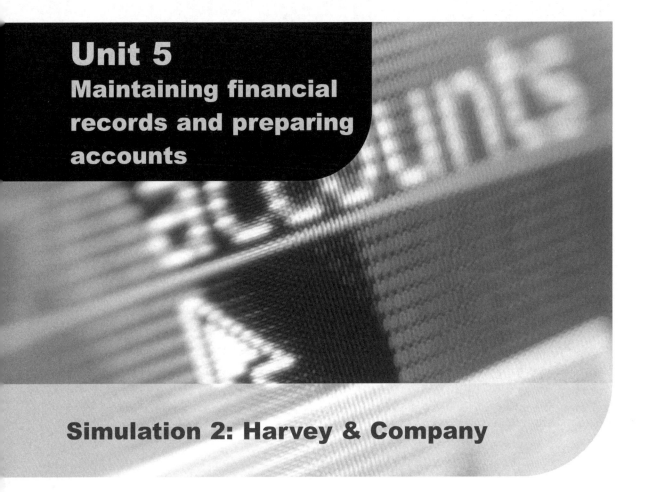

Unit 5
Maintaining financial records and preparing accounts

Simulation 2: Harvey & Company

NVQ Element coverage

5.2   collecting and collating information for the preparation of final accounts

5.3   preparing the final accounts of sole traders and partnerships

Scenario and contents

This Simulation is based on Harvey & Company, a sole trader business which is a retailer of pine furniture. The tasks include:

- correction of errors
- explaining the correction of errors
- making year end adjustments
- extending the trial balance
- the preparation of profit and loss account and balance sheet
- preparing control accounts
- calculating the cost of stock which has been stolen
- justifying the method of stock valuation

Suggested time allocation: three hours

SIMULATION 2
HARVEY & COMPANY

SITUATION

Your name is Kim Barnett and you work as the accounts assistant for the firm Harvey and Company which is a retailer of pine furniture. The business buys furniture from manufacturers and sells to members of the public on cash terms and to furniture shops on credit terms. The business is owned by Neil Harvey, who is a sole trader. One of your main duties is the preparation of the accounts in readiness for checking by the accounts supervisor, Chris Adams. Chris also acts as your line manager. There is another person who works as part of the accounts team: Martin Speight, who has recently joined as an accounts trainee.

This simulation relates to Harvey and Company's accounting year to 31 March 2004, today's date being 14 April 2004. The company maintains a full main ledger accounts with manual ledger accounts. It is registered for VAT, all sales being standard rated. A computer system is used for stock records.

This Simulation is divided into two parts. There are seven tasks relating to part 1 and four tasks relating to part 2.

You are allowed 3 hours to complete the tasks in both parts. You are advised to spend approximately two hours on Part 1 and one hour on Part 2.

TASKS

This Simulation is designed to let you show your ability to maintain financial records and prepare accounts.

You should read the whole Simulation before you start work, so that you are fully aware of what you will have to do.

The Simulation is divided into two parts and 11 tasks as follows:

PART ONE

Ledger accounting and the trial balance

Preparation of profit and loss account and balance sheet

You should spend about two hours on this part

Task 1

Prepare journal entries (narratives not required) for the errors and omissions listed on pages 103 to 104. Use the journal provided on page 107.

Task 2

Prepare a suspense account (page 108) showing the opening balance as per the original trial balance and the adjustments made with regard to the journal entries prepared as part of Task 1 above.

Task 3

Enter the journal entries calculated in Task 1 into the adjustments columns of the extended trial balance (pages 110 to 111). Do not total the adjustments columns at this stage.

Task 4

Certain errors occur in book-keeping which will not affect the balancing of a trial balance. Some of these errors were seen in Task 1 above. For the benefit of the new accounts trainee, Martin Speight, briefly outline any four such errors which are not detected in the book-keeping process. Use the memorandum form on page 109.

Task 5

Refer to the memorandum from Chris Adams on the next page.

- Show your calculation of the closing stock valuation at 31 March 2004. Use page 112 for your answer.

- Enter the year end adjustments into the adjustments columns of the extended trial balance (pages 110 to 111). Note: you are not required to show the journal entries for these transactions.

Task 6

Extend the trial balance (pages 110 to 111). This includes totalling all columns of the trial balance and making entries to record the net profit or loss for the year ended 31 March 2004 and the figures for the balance sheet at that date.

Task 7

Taking the figures from the extended trial balance, prepare the final accounts of Harvey & Company for the year ended 31 March 2004 in proper form, using the conventional format. Page 113 is for the trading and profit and loss account, and page 114 is for the balance sheet.

Data For Part 1

A list of balances has been provided, and written into the opening columns of the extended trial balance page 110). At present the opening trial balance does not agree; the difference has been posted to a suspense account. On investigation, you discover the following errors and omissions have been made:

(a) An insurance refund for £240 has been debited in the bank account, but not posted to insurance account.

(b) The drawings account totalling £8,308 for the year has been completely omitted from the list of balances.

(c) Purchases account has been overcast by £10,000.

(d) A second-hand delivery van was purchased during the year for £3,000 (net of VAT) and this has been posted inadvertently to the motor expenses account.

(e) Some packaging costing a total of £140 would be better described as printing and stationery expenses.

(f) The trial balance drawn up does not include the cash sales for the last day of the financial period which were banked late in the afternoon; the total receipts amounted to £3,525 inclusive of VAT.

(g) A payment for advertising by cheque for £1,256 has been credited in the bank account, but no corresponding debit entry has been made.

The following memorandum is received from Chris Adams:

MEMO

To: Kim Barnett, Accounts Assistant

From: Chris Adams, Accounts Supervisor

Subject: Year end adjustments

Date: 13 April 2004

The following year end adjustments need to be made before completing the extended trial balance as at 31 March:

(a) Depreciation is to be provided as follows:

- buildings – 2% per annum straight-line method

- vehicles – 25% per annum reducing balance method

- fixtures and fittings – 10% per annum straight-line method

(b) A bad debt of £500 is to be written off.

(c) Provision for doubtful debts is to be reduced by £600.

(d) £1,250 is owed in wages on 31 March 2004.

(e) Rates are prepaid by £450 on 31 March 2004.

(f) The computer records for stock give a closing valuation of £63,295 at cost price. We have had to reduce some items in price after the financial year end. The details are as follows:

Stock code	Quantity in stock 31 March 2004	Cost £	Normal selling price £	Reduced selling price £
CHS	10	30.00	45.00	30.00
DRW	10	80.00	120.00	60.00
TBY	8	50.00	75.00	37.50

PART TWO

Preparing control accounts

Calculating the cost of stolen stock

You should spend about one hour on this part; the data for the tasks is given below, and on the next page.

Task 8

Prepare a purchases ledger control account and ascertain the value of purchases made on credit for the period 1 April 2004 to 13 April 2004. A control account for completion is on page 115.

Task 9

Prepare a sales ledger control account for the same period, to calculate the credit sales figure. A control account for completion is on page 115.

Task 10

Calculate the cost of the stock stolen so that the correct insurance claim can be made by Harvey & Company. You can use the pro-forma trading account on page 116 – there is space below for your workings. Note: work to the nearest £.

Task 11

Since performing the calculations in Task 10 Martin Speight approaches you and asks:

"Why can't the insurance claim submitted to the brokers be calculated on its sales value rather than cost. After all, Harvey and Company would have been able to sell all of the furniture at retail price and not at the price at which they bought them."

Write a suitable reply to Martin on the memorandum provided on page 117. Your comments should relate to relevant accounting concepts and standards.

DATA FOR PART 2

You have just heard that there was a theft of stock from the warehouse last night (13 April 2004) but it is not clear how much has been stolen. Chris Adams has asked you to estimate what has been taken so that an insurance claim can be made straightaway. No double-entry records have been written up for April as yet because accounts staff are still involved with the year end accounts. However, the following information is available:

	as at 1 April 2004	as at 13 April 2004
	£	£
Stock at cost	use figures from	?
Trade creditors	final accounts at	13,465
Trade debtors	31 March 2004	18,250

The following transactions have been summarised from the cash book from 1 April 2004 to 13 April 2004.

	£
Cash purchases	1,450
Paid to creditors	5,750
Received from debtors	16,560
Cash sales	4,230
Discount allowed	856
Discount received	575

On 14 April 2004, before trading recommenced, a quick stock take was made based on the goods which were left in the warehouse after the theft. These are estimated to be worth £45,000 at cost.

Harvey and Company has a pricing policy of applying a mark-up of 50% on the cost of pine furniture purchased.

ANSWER PAGES

Task 1

JOURNAL			
	Details	**Dr** £	**Cr** £
(a)			
(b)			
(c)			
(d)			
(e)			
(f)			
(g)			

Task 2

Dr				SUSPENSE ACCOUNT	Cr
Date	Details	Amount	Date	Details	Amount
2004		£	2004 1 April	Balance b/d	£ 676

Task 4

MEMO
To:
From:
Subject: Errors not affecting a Trial Balance
Date:

Tasks 3, 4 and 6: **Extended Trial Balance**

account name	ledger balances	
	Dr	Cr
	£	£
Advertising	3,245	
Administration expenses	15,617	
Bad debts written off	2,000	
Discount allowed	3,468	
Discount received		1,012
Insurance	4,890	
Motor expenses	12,782	
Packaging costs	2,540	
Purchases	286,312	
Printing and stationery	1,667	
Rates	3,330	
Sales		418,451
Wages and salaries	50,942	
Buildings at cost	120,000	
Provision for depreciation: buildings		12,000
Vehicles at cost	28,000	
Provision for depreciation: vehicles		14,000
Fixtures and fittings at cost	35,000	
Provision for depreciation: fixtures etc		10,500
Opening stock	67,983	
Debtors	24,000	
Provision for doubtful debts		3,600
Bank		4,724
Trade creditors		12,165
VAT		8,765
Inland Revenue		2,883
Capital		173,000
Suspense		676
Total	661,776	661,776

name	Harvey & Company		date 31 March 2004			

adjustments		profit and loss account		balance sheet	
Dr £	Cr £	Dr £	Cr £	Dr £	Cr £

Task 5

Stock valuation at 31 March 2004

Task 7

HARVEY & COMPANY

TRADING AND PROFIT AND LOSS ACCOUNT

for the year ended 31 March 2004

	£	£

Task 7, continued

HARVEY & COMPANY

BALANCE SHEET

as at 31 March 2004

	£	£	£

Task 8

Dr   **PURCHASES LEDGER CONTROL ACCOUNT**   Cr

Date	Details	Amount	Date	Details	Amount
2004		£	2004		£

Task 9

Dr   **SALES LEDGER CONTROL ACCOUNT**   Cr

Date	Details	Amount	Date	Details	Amount
2004		£	2004		£

Task 10

TRADING ACCOUNT FOR THE PERIOD 1 APRIL 2004 TO 13 APRIL 2004

	£	£	£
Cash Sales			
Credit Sales			
Total sales			
Opening Stock			
Cash Purchases			
Credit Purchases			
less Closing Stock			
Cost of sales			
Gross profit			

Workings

Task 11

MEMO
To:
From:
Subject: Stock Valuation Insurance Claim
Date:

Page for workings

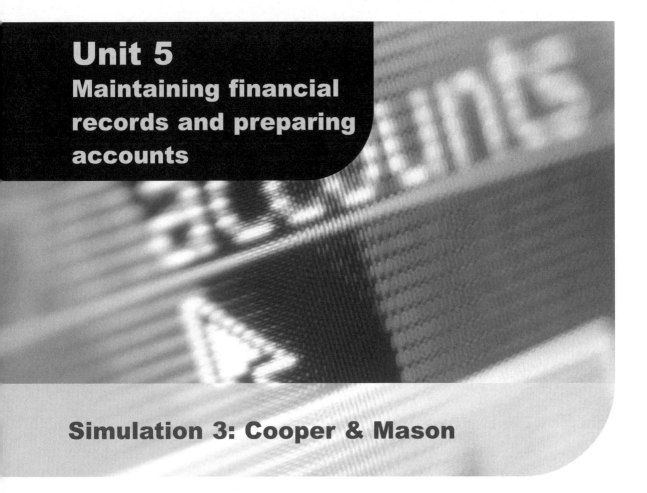

Unit 5
Maintaining financial records and preparing accounts

Simulation 3: Cooper & Mason

NVQ Element coverage

5.2   collecting and collating information for the preparation of final accounts

5.3   preparing the final accounts of sole traders and partnerships

Scenario and contents

This Simulation is based on work carried out at Cooper & Mason, a firm of accountants. The tasks involve dealing with four clients:

■   Rashid Lateef – adjusting for accruals and prepayments

■   Andrew Roberts – correction of errors and reconciliation of sales ledger control account

■   James Belushi – dealing with incomplete records

■   Marston and Banks – preparing a partnership appropriation account and balance sheet, and dealing with partnership changes

Suggested time allocation: four hours

SIMULATION 3
COOPER & MASON

SITUATION

You are employed by a firm of accountants, Cooper & Mason, as an accounts assistant. Your duties predominantly involve the preparation of final accounts – from either incomplete records or a trial balance. You also perform other duties such as basic book-keeping. Your line manager is the accounts supervisor, Lesley Dawson. Today's date is 24 May 2004

This Simulation is designed to let you show your ability to maintain financial records and prepare accounts.

You should read the whole Simulation before you start work, so that you are fully aware of what you will have to do.

DATA FOR CLIENT 1 – RASHID LATEEF

Rashid Lateef, one of your clients, has just submitted his accounts, which need adjusting for the relevant accruals and prepayments.

Rashid owns a window cleaning business and his accounts are usually relatively straightforward to prepare.

Set out below is a list of expenditure Rashid has incurred during the year, together with a list of opening and closing balances.

Rashid's accounting year end is 31 March.

Rashid is not registered for VAT purposes as his annual turnover is below the current threshold.

RENT PAYABLE

Rashid rents a lock-up garage, a place in which he can store his van and ladders overnight. Rashid pays for the garage quarterly in advance. At 1 April 2003 Rashid had already paid in advance for the two months to 31 May 2003, a total of £300. The agreement is re-negotiated each year on 1 March.

During the year the business paid the following quarterly instalments:

		£
2 June 2003	by cheque (to 31 August 2003)	450
1 September 2003	by cheque (to 30 November 2003)	450
7 December 2003	by cheque (to 29 February 2004)	450
6 March 2004	by cheque (to 31 May 2004)	525

PUBLIC LIABILITY INSURANCE

Rashid pays for his insurance quarterly in arrears. He has signed a direct debit mandate to ensure he keeps his account up-to-date at all times. The renewal date of the policy is 1 November each year.

At the start of this accounting year Rashid owed two months' payments totalling £60.

During the year the following quarterly payments were made:

		£
1 May 2003	by direct debit	90
2 August 2003	by direct debit	90
1 November 2003	by direct debit	90
1 February 2004	by direct debit	105

TASK

Task 1.1

Write up the main ledger accounts for Rashid Lateef showing clearly the opening and closing balances, the amounts paid during the year as well as the correct transfers to be made to profit and loss account. Use the ledger accounts on the next page.

ANSWER PAGE

Task 1.1

Dr   **RENT PAYABLE ACCOUNT**   Cr

Date	Details	Amount £	Date	Details	Amount £

Dr   **PUBLIC LIABILITY INSURANCE ACCOUNT**   Cr

Date	Details	Amount £	Date	Details	Amount £

DATA FOR CLIENT 2 – ANDREW ROBERTS

One of your colleagues is trying to reconcile the sales ledger control account to the subsidiary (sales) ledger balances, but unfortunately he is not having much luck. This tends to be a perennial problem as the client, Mr Andrew Roberts of Pentium Products, does not always balance his books off properly. Often the telephone rings or he is suddenly called out of the office on emergency business and, as a consequence, he forgets what he has completed in the ledger and this is where things start to get messy.

Below are the figures from the sales ledger control account, as supplied by your colleague.

SALES LEDGER CONTROL ACCOUNT FOR THE YEAR TO 29 FEBRUARY 2004			
	£		£
Balance b/d	138,870	Debtor receipts	449,817
Credit sales	478,110	Discount allowed	19,053
		Sales returns	5,115
		Bad debts written off	7,977
		Purchase ledger contra	74,274
		Balance c/d	60,744
	616,980		616,980
Balance b/d	60,744		

You have also received a list of individual debtor balances, which have been supplied directly by Mr Roberts, and these total £30,338. However, a thorough check of the book-keeping reveals the following errors and omissions:

1   One of the pages in the sales day book has been added up incorrectly, the total being carried forward as £52,334 instead of the correct amount of £25,334

2   Certain bad debts have been written off in the control account, but no entries have been made in the subsidiary accounts. The bad debts which need adjustment total £2,412.

3   A debtor balance of £5,668 has been completely omitted from the list of individual balances.

4   A cash refund of £3,450 given to a debtor, CRK Limited, for faulty goods supplied has been adjusted on the individual list of balances but no entry has been made in the sales ledger control account.

5   The subsidiary ledger account of Explore PLC has been listed as a debit balance of £13,740 instead of the correct amount of £17,340.

TASKS

2.1   Make any adjustments that you think are necessary in order to reconcile the sales ledger control account against the individual list of customer balances. Use the blank forms on the next page.

2.2   For some time the accounts supervisor has been encouraging Mr Roberts to convert from a manual book-keeping system to a computerised one. Draft a letter to Mr Roberts explaining the advantages such a system could bring to his business. Use the letter heading on page 125. The letter will be signed by the supervisor, Lesley Dawson.

ANSWER PAGES

Task 2.1

Dr						
Date	Details	Amount	Date	Details		Amount
2004 29 Feb	Balance b/d	£ 60,744	2004			£

SALES LEDGER CONTROL ACCOUNT — Cr

CUSTOMER BALANCES LISTING

	£
Balance b/d	30,338

Task 2.2

COOPER & MASON, ACCOUNTANTS

14 Leigh Brook Road
Upper Hatherley
Cheltenham GL52 4RR
Tel 01242 576042 Fax 01242 567424
Email mail@cooper&mason.co.uk

Terry Cooper FCCA,   Gary Mason ACCA

DATA FOR CLIENT 3 – JAMES BELUSHI

A new set of books has come into the office of Cooper & Mason for the preparation of financial statements. They are from James Belushi, a sole trader, who is in the confectionery packaging business. He purchases paper and cardboard and converts these items into chocolate boxes which he sells to the sweet manufacturing industry. He operates from a warehouse in Leigh Sinton but most of the boxes are folded and packaged by a series of outworkers who work from home. James does not maintain a full set of accounting records but the following list of balances has been supplied; the balances relate to the start and end of his current financial year.

JAMES BELUSHI: ACCOUNT BALANCES		
	1 May 2003 £	30 April 2004 £
Warehouse (cost £100,000)	80,000	78,000
Motor van (cost £22,000)	16,500	12,375
Warehouse equipment (cost £16,000)	12,000	9,000
Stock at cost	6,250	5,490
Trade debtors	8,370	10,420
Prepayments		
motor van expenses	400	375
business insurances	150	225
business rates	260	650
Bank	7,250	5,880
Cash	250	400
Trade creditors	9,330	8,670
Accruals		
heat and light	750	590
telephone	180	410
wages	3,150	4,660

Mr Belushi maintains the bank account and cash account himself. He has provided you with the summarised cash book shown on the next page.

The cash book has been balanced and agreed to the bank statements and the cash float.

JAMES BELUSHI – CASH BOOK SUMMARY

RECEIPTS	CASH	BANK
	£	£
Balances brought down	250	7,250
Cash sales	13,400	8,600
Receipts from debtors	2,890	157,750
Cash banked	–	8,250
TOTAL	16,540	181,850

PAYMENTS	CASH	BANK
	£	£
Cash purchases	1,970	–
Drawings	1,900	28,590
General expenses	350	3,110
Telephone	–	2,850
Wages	2,480	24,660
Cash banked	8,250	–
Paid to creditors	–	82,370
Heat and light	–	4,330
Motor van expenses	960	8,440
Business insurances	–	11,120
Business rates	–	7,140
Advertising	–	2,400
Machine repairs	230	960
Balances carried down	400	5,880
TOTAL	16,540	181,850

TASKS

Task 3.1

Calculate James Belushi's opening capital balance at 1 May 2003, using the statement of assets and liabilities on the next page.

Task 3.2

Calculate the figure for credit sales for the year. Use the sales ledger control account on page 130.

Task 3.3

Calculate the figure for credit purchases for the year. Use the purchases ledger control account on page 130.

Task 3.4

Prepare a trading, profit and loss account for the year to 30 April 2004. Use the layout provided on page 131.

Task 3.5

Prepare a balance sheet as at 30 April 2004. Use the layout provided on page 132.

Task 3.6

When Mr Belushi submitted the books to you he said that he had worked out that he had made a loss this year. He has concluded this from the fact that his business bank account went down from £7,250 to £5,880 during the year, and this is a good indicator with regard to profitability.

Draft a letter to Mr Belushi to be sent out to him with the accounts which responds to his comments. Use the letter head on page 133. You should make specific reference to the accounting concepts that are relevant in the calculation of profit. The letter will be signed by your supervisor, Lesley Dawson.

ANSWER PAGES

Task 3.1

STATEMENT OF ASSETS AND LIABILITIES
as at 1 May 2003

	assets £	liabilities £

Task 3.2

Dr				SALES LEDGER CONTROL ACCOUNT		Cr
Date	Details	Amount	Date	Details		Amount
		£				£

Task 3.3

Dr				PURCHASES LEDGER CONTROL ACCOUNT		Cr
Date	Details	Amount	Date	Details		Amount
		£				£

Task 3.4

JAMES BELUSHI
TRADING AND PROFIT AND LOSS ACCOUNT FOR THE YEAR TO _____

	£	£	£
Cash sales			
Credit sales			
Total sales			
Opening stock			
Cash purchases			
Credit purchases			
Total purchases			
less Closing stock			
Cost of sales			
Gross profit			
Overheads			
General expenses			
Telephone			
Wages			
Heat and light			
Motor van expenses			
Business insurances			
Business rates			
Advertising			
Machine repairs			
Depreciation:			
warehouse			
motor van			
machinery			
Net profit/ (loss) for the year			

Task 3.5

JAMES BELUSHI

BALANCE SHEET AS AT ....

	Cost	Provision for depreciation	Net
	£	£	£
FIXED ASSETS			
Warehouse			
Motor van			
Warehouse machinery			
CURRENT ASSETS			
Stock			
Trade debtors			
Bank			
Cash			
Prepayments			
CURRENT LIABILITIES			
Trade creditors			
Accruals			
NET CURRENT ASSETS			
TOTAL NET ASSETS			
REPRESENTED BY:			
CAPITAL			
Balance at 1 May 2003			
Add net profit/(loss) for the year			
Less drawings			

Task 3.6

COOPER & MASON, ACCOUNTANTS

14 Leigh Brook Road
Upper Hatherley
Cheltenham GL52 4RR
Tel 01242 576042 Fax 01242 567424
Email mail@cooper&mason.co.uk

Terry Cooper FCCA,   Gary Mason ACCA

DATA FOR CLIENT 4 – MARSTON AND BANKS

The accounts of the partnership of Pete Marston and Tony Banks have been passed to you for completion. Marston and Banks own a shop which sells household goods.

Their partnership agreement allows for the following:

Partners' salaries

- Marston £12,000
- Banks £10,000

Interest on capital

- 5% per annum on the balance at the year end

Profit share

- Marston 60%
- Banks 40%

A colleague has prepared the partnership trial balance after completion of their trading and profit and loss account (for the year to 30 April 2004) as follows:

	Dr	Cr
	£	£
Buildings at cost	120,000	
Provision for depreciation - buildings		24,000
Fixtures and fittings at cost	30,000	
Provision for depreciation - fixtures and fittings		13,500
Delivery van at cost	28,000	
Provision for depreciation - delivery van		7,000
Trade creditors		14,050
Value Added Tax		4,200
Cash	400	
Bank	3,650	
Closing stock	19,750	
Bank loan		33,500
Capital accounts: Marston		50,000
Banks		30,000
Current accounts: Marston	150	
Banks		12,300
Drawings: Marston	22,500	
Banks	15,250	
Net profit for the year		51,150
	239,700	239,700

TASKS

Task 4.1

Prepare the appropriation account for the partnership for the year ended 30 April 2004. Use the layout on page 136.

Task 4.2

Update the current accounts for the partners. Use the layout on page 136.

Task 4.3

Prepare the partnership balance sheet as at 30 April 2004. Use the layout on page 137.

ADDITIONAL DATA

On 1 May 2004 Jane Mitchell was admitted into the partnership.

The profit sharing ratios are now Marston (3), Banks (2) and Mitchell (1). Goodwill has been agreed at a valuation of £30,000. Jane Mitchell has brought £20,000 of cash into the business as her capital and premium for goodwill. Goodwill is to be written off in the accounts.

TASKS

Task 4.4

Prepare the partners' capital accounts to record the admission of Jane Mitchell as a partner. Show clearly the balances carried down. Use the layout on page 138.

Task 4.5

Write a note to a trainee who is assisting you which explains the changes you have made to the partners' capital accounts. Use page 139 for your note.

ANSWER PAGES

Task 4.1

PETE MARSTON AND TONY BANKS

Appropriation account for the year ended 30 April 2004

	£	£
Net profit		
Salaries:		
Marston		
Banks		
Interest on capital:		
Marston		
Banks		
Balance of net profit		
Share of profit:		
Marston		
Banks		

Task 4.2

CURRENT ACCOUNTS

2004		Marston £	Banks £	2004		Marston £	Banks £
1 Apr	Balance b/f	150		1 Apr	Balance b/f		12,300

Task 4.3

PETE MARSTON AND TONY BANKS

Balance sheet at 30 April 2004

	£	£
Fixed assets:		
Buildings		
Fixtures and fittings		
Delivery van		
Current assets:		
Stock		
Bank		
Cash		
Current liabilities:		
Creditors		
VAT		
Net current assets		
Long-term liabilities		
Bank loan		
Total net assets		
Capital accounts:		
Marston		
Banks		
Current accounts:		
Marston		
Banks		

Task 4.4

CAPITAL ACCOUNTS

Date 2004		Marston £	Banks £	Mitchell £
1 May	Balances b/d	50,000	30,000	

Date 2004		Marston £	Banks £	Mitchell £

Task 4.5

Note to trainee

Page for workings

Unit 5
Maintaining financial records and preparing accounts

Simulation 4: Adcock & Tweed

NVQ Element coverage

5.2   collecting and collating information for the preparation of final accounts

5.3   preparing the final accounts of sole traders and partnerships

Scenario and contents

This Simulation is based on work carried out at Adcock & Tweed, a firm of accountants. The tasks involve dealing with three clients:

■   Andy Gillman – correction of errors and preparation of final accounts, using the extended trial balance method and in proper form

■   Alan Partridge – adjusting for accruals and prepayments

■   Bon Voyage Limited – correction of errors and reconciliation of purchases ledger control account

Suggested time allocation: three hours

SIMULATION 4
ADCOCK & TWEED

This Simulation is designed to let you show your ability to maintain financial records and prepare accounts.

You should read the whole Simulation before you start work, so that you are fully aware of what you will have to do.

SITUATION

You are employed by a firm of accountants, Adcock & Tweed, as an accounts assistant. Your duties are quite varied and include the preparation of final accounts ready for checking by the accounts supervisor, Juanita Martinez. You are also responsible for the work of an accounts trainee, Jim Basinger. Today's date is 24 January 2005. Your main tasks for the day are dealing with the accounts of three major clients.

DATA FOR CLIENT 1 – ANDY GILLMAN

Andy Gillman, one of your clients, is a sole trader who buys and sells recorded music from 'Andy's Place', a shop at 57 High Street, Persham WR5 3XY. The majority of his sales are for cash, although he does give credit to the local disc jockeys in the area.

Andy has some knowledge of accounting but his accounts system is relatively simple, with all accounts contained in a main ledger. Unfortunately his latest trial balance does not agree, and the difference has been posted to a suspense account.

Upon investigation the following errors have been discovered:

- An error of transposition has taken place in the motor expenses account. The total for this account should read as £1,530 instead of its brought down figure of £1,350.

- A second-hand computer was bought during the year to assist with the office procedures as well as introducing some system of stock control. Its cost of £500 has currently been analysed to purchases.

- A payment made to a local club for advertising has been credited to the bank account for £98, but no corresponding entry has been made.

- A credit note for £120 received from a supplier for goods returned has been debited to the supplier's account, but again no other entry has been made.

- Finally, a payment totalling £150 made for the purchase of CDs has been credited to the bank account but then inadvertently credited again to the sales account.

TASKS FOR CLIENT 1: ANDY GILLMAN

Task 1.1

Provide journal entries for the errors listed above in order to clear the suspense account. You can use the journal layout provided on page 145. Note that narratives are not required.

Task 1.2

Further adjustments are required in order to complete the accounts. Note: you are not required to show the journal entries for these adjustments.

Depreciation rates are calculated using the straight-line method based on cost as follows:

Motor vehicles	25%
Buildings	5%
Fixtures and fittings	20%
Office equipment	20%

Andy finds that disc jockeys are notoriously bad payers who are quite likely to move on or disappear without any notice. The provision for bad debts should therefore be maintained at 10% of the closing debtors figure at all times.

Closing stock is valued at a cost of £4,350, but there are some Acid Jazz CDs which are proving hard to sell. The consignment originally cost £460 but will have to be marked down as a sale item and sold for £300 in total.

Other adjustments relating to year end procedures are as follows:

Accrued expenditure as at 31 December 2004

Light and heat	£50
Salaries and wages	£70
General expenses	£20

Prepaid expenses as at 31 December 2004

Rates	£50
Insurance	£90
Motor expenses	£110

You are required to prepare an extended trial balance (pages 146 to 147) for Andy Gillman in order to show his net profit or loss for the year ended 31 December 2004 and the figures for his balance sheet at that date.

Task 1.3

Taking the figures from the extended trial balance, prepare the final accounts of 'Andy's Place' for the year ended 31 December 2004 in proper form, using the conventional format. Page 148 is for the trading and profit and loss account, and page 149 is for the balance sheet.

Task 1.4

Draft a letter to Andy Gillman explaining why the stock valuation at the end of December 2004 was adjusted. You should refer to the relevant accounting standards and concepts. Use the letterhead on page 150. The letter will be signed by your supervisor, Juanita Martinez.

ANSWER PAGES

Task 1.1

JOURNAL		
Details	**Dr** **£**	**Cr** **£**

Task 1.2 ANDY GILLMAN TRADING AS 'ANDY'S PLACE' – Extended Trial Balance

account name	ledger balances	
	Dr	Cr
	£	£
Sales		42,500
Purchases	20,750	
Salaries and wages	1,500	
Motor expenses	1,350	
Rates	1,010	
Light and heat	695	
Cleaning and maintenance	425	
Advertising	360	
Stock	2,150	
Trade debtors	2,050	
Provision for doubtful debts		316
Decrease in provision for doubtful debts		
Cash	100	
Bank	650	
Trade creditors		4,350
Bank loan		5,000
Buildings (cost)	50,000	
Fixtures and fittings (cost)	2,500	
Motor vehicles (cost)	8,000	
Office equipment (cost)	1,500	
Buildings: provision for depreciation		5,000
Fixtures and fittings: provision for depreciation		750
Motor vehicles: Provision for Depreciation		4,000
Office Equipment: provision for depreciation		150
Depreciation - buildings		
Depreciation - fixtures & fittings		
Depreciation - motor vehicles		
Depreciation - office equipment		
Sales returns	450	
Drawings	12,000	
Purchases returns		690
General expenses	965	
Insurance	1,225	
Loan interest	168	
Accruals		
Prepayments		
Capital		45,550
Suspense	458	
Net profit/ loss		
	108,306	108,306

date **31 December 2004**

adjustments		profit and loss		balance sheet	
Dr £	Cr £	Dr £	Cr £	Dr £	Cr £

Task 1.3

ANDY GILLMAN, TRADING AS 'ANDY'S PLACE'

TRADING AND PROFIT AND LOSS ACCOUNT

for the year ended 31 December 2004

	£	£	£

Task 1.3, continued

ANDY GILLMAN, TRADING AS 'ANDY'S PLACE'

BALANCE SHEET

as at 31 December 2004

	£	£	£

Task 1.4

ADCOCK & TWEED, ACCOUNTANTS
29 Union Street
Eveshore
WR6 5HN
Tel 01905 748888 Fax 01905 748934
Email mail@adcock&tweed.co.uk

Graham Adcock FCCA,   Jennifer Tweed ACCA

DATA FOR CLIENT 2 – ALAN PARTRIDGE

An accounts trainee is working on the year end accounts of one of your clients, Alan Partridge. The trainee asks for your help in making the adjustments for accruals and prepayments.

Alan Partridge runs a landscape and gardening business in Persham, operating from an industrial unit near the railway station. In this unit he stores his equipment and carries out repairs to mowers and other garden machinery. The address is Unit 16, Avon Industrial Estate, Persham, WR3 7YG.

Set out below is a list of the business overheads which Mr Partridge has incurred during the year, together with details of opening and closing balances. Alan's accounting year end is 31 December.

HEAT AND LIGHT

At the start of the 2004 financial year there was a balance of £546 outstanding on the electricity account.

During the year the business made the following payments:

		£
21.01.04	by cheque	827
24.04.04	by cheque	959
15.07.04	by cash	633
27.10.04	by cash	472

It has now been estimated by the electricity company that Mr Partridge owes a further £347 for the period to 31.12.04.

ADVERTISING

Alan Partridge has an account with the local newspaper, the Persham Voice, to advertise in their classified section. He pays for this quarterly in advance. At 31 December 2003 Mr Partridge had already paid £600 in advance for the two months to February 2004. The agreement is renegotiated every six months.

During the year the business paid the following quarterly instalments:

		£
02.03.04	by cheque (to May 2004)	900
01.06.04	by cheque (to August 2004)	1,050
07.09.04	by cheque (to November 2004)	1,050
06.12.04	by cheque (to February 2005)	1,125

TELEPHONE

Mr Partridge's telephone operates on the Orion system and, as part of an introductory offer to businesses in the area, the telephone company is currently supplying the line rental free for the next two years. This means that businesses such as Alan's only pay for the calls made on the telephone line.

At the start of this accounting year it was estimated that Alan owed £214 for calls.

During the year the following quarterly payments were made:

		£
21.02.04	by direct debit	504
26.05.04	by direct debit	667
24.08.04	by direct debit	496
29.11.04	by direct debit	571

No details are available at present as to what calls have been made for the period 30.11.04 to 31.12.04, but looking at the previous quarter's bill and last year's accrual, you have estimated this to be £189.

RENT RECEIVED

To provide additional income to the business, Alan sub-lets the first-floor office part of the industrial unit to another trader, Susan Wilkinson, who uses it for her secretarial business 'Temps Galore'. As this name suggests, she provides temporary secretarial cover to businesses in the area.

The rental agreement has been fixed for a three year period to 28.02.2006 at £9,000 per annum. At the start of the current year (1 January 2004), Sue owed Alan one month's rent.

Unfortunately, throughout the year she proved rather unreliable with the quarterly payments and the following was received by Alan on the dates given:

		£
06.01.04	cash	1,500
03.05.04	cash	3,000
07.09.04	cheque	3,750
31.10.04	bank giro credit	3,000

TASKS FOR CLIENT 2: ALAN PARTRIDGE

Task 2.1

Write up the main ledger accounts for Alan Partridge showing clearly the opening and closing balances, the amounts paid/received during the year as well as the transfers to be made to the profit and loss account. Use the main ledger accounts shown on the next two pages.

Task 2.2

Alan Partridge does not understand why he has to submit his books to you each year, to have them adjusted for the closing accruals and prepayments. After all this costs him money and after a period of time he reckons you could quite easily base the financial statements on the amounts paid and received during the year.

Respond to this comment of Alan's on the letter head on page 155. Your reply should mention the relevant accounting concepts and conventions. The letter will be signed by your supervisor, Juanita Martinez.

ANSWER PAGES

Task 2.1

Dr **HEAT AND LIGHT ACCOUNT** Cr

Date	Details	Amount	Date	Details	Amount
		£			£

Dr **ADVERTISING ACCOUNT** Cr

Date	Details	Amount	Date	Details	Amount
		£			£

Task 2.1, continued

Dr				TELEPHONE ACCOUNT		Cr
Date	Details	Amount	Date	Details		Amount
		£				£

Dr				RENT RECEIVED ACCOUNT		Cr
Date	Details	Amount	Date	Details		Amount
		£				£

Task 2.2

ADCOCK & TWEED, ACCOUNTANTS

29 Union Street

Eveshore

WR6 5HN

Tel 01905 748888 Fax 01905 748934

Email mail@adcock&tweed.co.uk

Graham Adcock FCCA,   Jennifer Tweed ACCA

DATA FOR CLIENT 3 – BON VOYAGE LIMITED

You are working on the accounts of one of your clients, Bon Voyage Limited. You customarily carry out a reconciliation of the purchase ledger control account against the individual creditors' accounts in the subsidiary (purchases) ledger. The control account is in the main ledger, while the creditors' accounts are in the subsidiary ledger.

You have delegated the reconciliation to the accounts trainee, Jim Basinger. He has prepared the following purchase ledger control account but, unfortunately, it does not agree with the individual list of creditors' account balances from the subsidiary ledger.

PURCHASE LEDGER CONTROL ACCOUNT FOR THE YEAR TO 31 DECEMBER 2004			
	£		£
Paid to suppliers	867,990	Balance b/d	104,871
Discount received	25,660	Credit purchases	1,056,890
Purchases returns	33,250		
Sales ledger contra	75,890		
Balance c/d	158,971		
	1,161,761		1,161,761
		Balance b/d	158,971

The total of the individual balances in the subsidiary (purchases) ledger has been totalled at £209,521. However, a thorough check of the book-keeping reveals the following errors and omissions:

1   A debit balance of £14,780 on an individual creditor's account within the subsidiary ledger was included in the calculation of the total balances as though it was a credit balance.

2   One of the pages in the purchase day book was totalled incorrectly. The total was £18,000 less than the correct sum of the individual entries.

3   A credit note received from a supplier for £6,500 had been entered into the purchases returns day book as £5,600.

4   No entries had been made in the individual creditors' accounts to record some of the sales ledger contras. The transactions omitted totalled £12,080.

5   An individual creditor, High Density Limited, has been extracted as a credit balance of £23,230 instead of the correct credit balance of £32,320.

TASKS FOR CLIENT 3: BON VOYAGE LIMITED

Task 3.1

Make any entries that you consider are necessary to the purchase ledger control account and to the individual list of creditor balances. At the end of your adjustments, the two closing balances should reconcile.

Use the control account layout on the next page and the supplier balances listing form on page 158.

Task 3.2

Control accounts appear in most large businesses as part of the book-keeping process. One of the main reasons for this is that such accounts act as 'an aid to management.' Briefly explain to Jim Basinger, the accounts trainee, in what areas control accounts assist the management function within a business. Use the memorandum on page 159.

ANSWER PAGES

Task 3.1

PURCHASE LEDGER CONTROL ACCOUNT	
	£
	Balance b/d 158,971

Task 3.1, continued

SUPPLIER BALANCES LISTING	
	£
Balance b/d	209,521

Task 3.2

MEMO
To: **From:** **Subject:** **Date:**

Page for workings

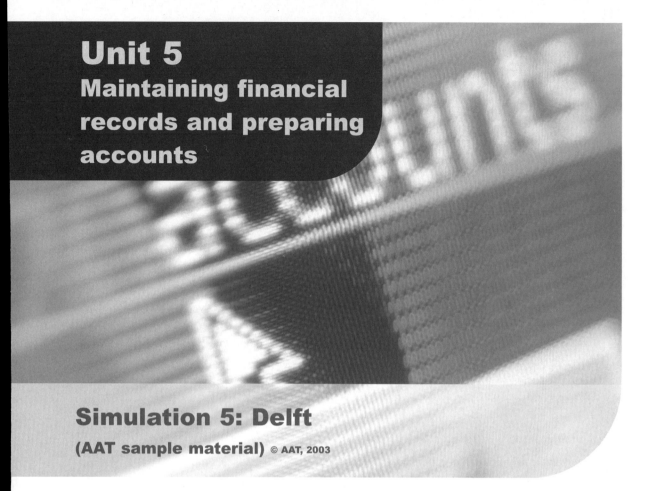

Unit 5
Maintaining financial records and preparing accounts

Simulation 5: Delft

(AAT sample material) © AAT, 2003

NVQ Element coverage

5.1 maintaining records relating to capital acquisition and disposal

5.2 collecting and collating information for the preparation of final accounts

5.3 preparing the final accounts of sole traders and partnerships

Scenario and contents

This Simulation is based on Delft, a partnership business which sells a range of high quality cutlery, glassware and china to the general public. The tasks include:

■ recording acquisitions and disposals in the fixed asset register

■ calculating depreciation amounts

■ journal entries

■ postings to the main ledger

■ reconciliation of purchases ledger control account

■ correction of errors, including the use of suspense account

■ stock valuation

■ extended trial balance

■ the preparation of a partnership profit and loss account (including an appropriation account) and a balance sheet

Suggested time allocation: four hours

SIMULATION 5
DELFT

SITUATION

Delft sells a range of high quality cutlery, glassware and china to the general public.

*   The business is owned and managed by a partnership. The partners are: Matthew Denby, Amina Iqbal and Jane Knight.

*   The partnership owns the shop premises.

*   The partnership employs one member of staff, Anne Thorpe, who carries out general administration and maintains the accounting records.

*   The business is registered for VAT and all sales are at the standard rate (17.5%).

Your name is Chris Stonham. You are employed by a local firm of Chartered Certified Accountants and have been assigned to help with the preparation of the annual accounts of Delft for the year ended 30 September 2003. You report to Sarah Bishop, a senior manager in the firm.

Accounting records

Delft maintains a full main ledger with manual ledger accounts in alphabetical order.

Today's date is 14 November 2003.

DATA AND TASKS

This Simulation is designed to let you show your ability to maintain financial records and prepare accounts.

You should read the whole Simulation before you start work, so that you are fully aware of what you will have to do.

The answer pages for the Tasks are on pages 174 to 200.

The Simulation is divided into two parts and twelve tasks as follows:

PART ONE

Accounting for fixed assets

Task 1   Fixed asset register – acquisitions and disposals

Task 2   Fixed assets – completeness

Task 3   Fixed asset register – depreciation calculation

Ledger accounting and the trial balance

Task 4   Posting of journals to the main ledger

Task 5   Reconciling the purchase ledger

Task 6   Balancing ledger accounts and preparing a trial balance

PART TWO

Adjusting and extending the trial balance

Task 7   Clearing the suspense account

Task 8   Calculating the value of closing stock

Task 9   Adjusting the trial balance

Task 10   Extending the trial balance and calculating net profit

Drafting final accounts

Task 11   Preparing an appropriation account and partners' current accounts

Task 12   Preparing a profit and loss account and a balance sheet

PART ONE TASKS

Part One includes Tasks 1 – 6. You should spend about two hours on this part.

Accounting for fixed assets

Background information

There are three groups of fixed assets:

	Type of asset	*Depreciation rate and method*
1	Shop premises	2% per year on cost (straight line basis);
2	Motor vehicles (delivery vans)	$33^1/_3$% per year on cost (straight line basis);
3	Equipment, fixtures and fittings	25% per year on net book value (reducing balance basis).

All acquisitions and disposals of fixed assets, except for shop premises, are recorded in a manual fixed asset register. This provides the following information about individual fixed assets and group of assets:

- details of capital expenditure (but not revenue expenditure) incurred in acquiring or enhancing fixed assets

- details of disposals

- depreciation calculations

The main ledger includes accounts for cost and accumulated depreciation for each category of fixed asset. The depreciation charge is recorded in a single expense account in the main ledger.

- Residual value is assumed to be nil in all cases.

- A full year's depreciation is charged in the year of an asset's acquisition, regardless of the exact date of acquisition.

- No depreciation is charged in the year of an asset's disposal.

- Motor vehicle running costs are recorded in the accounts as Delivery Express.

All acquisitions of fixed assets are authorised by a partner's signature on the invoice. All disposals are authorised by means of a memo from one of the partners. Jane Knight is the partner who is normally responsible for authorising acquisitions and disposals of fixed assets.

Task 1

Refer to the suppliers' invoices and the memo on pages 166 to 168. These relate to two purchases and one disposal. The invoices had not been entered in the accounts at 30 September 2003.

- Record the acquisitions and the disposal in the fixed asset register (pages 174 to 176).

- Prepare journals to record the invoices and the disposal in the main ledger. Use the journal on page 177.

Task 2

Anne Thorpe has listed the motor vehicles and items of equipment actually present at the shop at the close of business on 30 September 2003. Her list is on page 168.

- Compare this list with the details recorded in the fixed assets register and describe any discrepancies in a memo to Jane Knight. Use the memorandum form on page 178.

Task 3

- Calculate the depreciation for the year on the motor vehicles and on each item of equipment, fixtures and fittings and record the depreciation and net book values in the fixed asset register.

- Calculate the depreciation charge for the year on the shop premises. You will need to refer to ledger accounts on page 187. Use page 179 for your answer.

- Prepare journals on page 177 to record depreciation in the main ledger.

Ledger Accounting and the trial balance

Background Information

All sales are cash sales. There are no credit sales. The business does not keep a sales day book or subsidiary (sales) ledger.

All purchases are on credit. Purchases and purchase returns are recorded in the purchases day book. These are posted to the Purchase Ledger Control Account, the VAT Control Account and the Purchases Account in the main ledger.

Individual creditor accounts are kept in the subsidiary (purchase) ledger. The purchase ledger is not part of the double entry system.

Cash and cheques received and paid are recorded in a manual cash book. This is posted to the main ledger at the end of each month.

The purchase day book and the cash book have been written up and posted to the main ledger for the year to 30 September 2003.

Task 4

Post the journals that you have prepared in Tasks 1 and 3 to the main ledger on pages 180 to 189.

Task 5

Refer to the purchase day book on page 169, the subsidiary (purchase) ledger accounts on pages 169 and 170, and the purchase ledger control account on page 186.

*   List and total the balances on the purchase ledger accounts at 30 September 2003. Use the layout on page 190.

*   Compare this total with the balance on the purchase ledger control account at 30 September 2003. Establish the reason for the difference between the two. Prepare a journal on page 191 to correct any errors.

*   Post the journal entry on page 191 to the main ledger.

Task 6

*   Bring down a balance as at 30 September 2003 on each account in the main ledger.

*   Enter the balances in the first two columns of the extended trial balance (pages 192 to 193). The totals of the two columns will not be equal. Enter the difference in a suspense account on the face of the trial balance.

INVOICE

Wheeler Motors Limited

75-77 London Road
Chesterton CH2 3DN

Tel 02354 767777
Fax 02354 767888
VAT Reg 810 7842 81

customer:

J Knight
Delft
61 East Street
CHESTERTON
CH1 8QL

invoice no.   3150

date/tax point: 21 September 2003

description of sale
Ford Transit Van

Registration: WA53 SPO

Registration date: 21 September 2003

Stock no: Z78781   chassis No: AZCFCB   Engine No: ST89800

	£
List price	12,000.00
VAT at 17.5%	2,100.00
	14,100.00
Vehicle excise duty (12 months)	140.00
Total due	14,240.00
Less: part exchange allowance	(2,500.00)
Balance to pay	11,740.00

Terms: 30 days net

Approved for payment 3 October 2003
J A Knight.

INVOICE

Against the Grain

Unit 8, Wyvern Centre, Temperley, CHESTERTON CH5 9RH

Telephone: 02354 532876

Fax: 02354 532910

Email: orders@against-the-grain

Website: www.against-the-grain.com

VAT registration 719 0365 81

customer:	**invoice no.** 572
J Knight Delft 61 East Street CHESTERTON CH1 8QL	**date/tax point:** 26 September 2003

quantity	description	Net (£)	VAT (£)
1	Display Cabinet in polished English Ash	8,500.00	1,487.50
	VAT @ 17.5%	1,487.50	
	TOTAL	9,987.50	

Approved for payment 10 October 2003
J A Knight.

Terms: Payment is due 30 days from the invoice date

MEMO

To:	Anne Thorpe
From:	Jane Knight
Subject:	New delivery van
Date:	20 September 2003

I have ordered a new Ford delivery van from Wheeler Motors in part exchange for our oldest delivery van, registration number Z754 WIL. I shall let you have a copy of the purchase invoice once I have checked and approved it.

Jane

Fixed assets on the premises at 30 September 2003

Garage (at the rear of the shop)

Delivery van (WA53 SPO)

Office

Desktop PC (Dell)

Laser Printer (Samsung)

Laptop computer (Toshiba)

Shop

Display cabinet

Display tables

Cash register

Other fittings (built-in shelving and cupboards)

Purchase day book (September 2003)

Date		Net	VAT	Gross
		£	£	£
1 September	Fine Ceramics Ltd	5,090.55	890.84	5,981.39
1 September	Pentagon Glassware	7,337.83	1,284.12	8,621.95
5 September	Cutler and Co	5,380.00	941.50	6,321.50
9 September	Thrower Ltd	1,328.17	232.43	1,560.60
15 September	Pentagon Glassware	3,008.93	526.56	3,535.49
19 September	Thrower Ltd (Credit Note)	1,944.62	340.31	2,284.93
25 September	Fine Ceramics Ltd	3,779.50	661.42	4,440.92
		27,869.60	4,877.18	32,746.78

SUBSIDIARY (PURCHASE) LEDGER

Fine Ceramics Ltd

Date 2003	Details	Amount £	Date 2003	Details	Amount £
15 Sep	Bank	8,956.95	1 Sep	Balance b/f	13,709.61
15 Sep	Discount received	182.79	1 Sep	Purchase Day Book	5,981.39
30 Sep	Balance c/f	14,992.18	25 Sep	Purchase Day Book	4,440.92
		24,131.92			24,131.92
			1 Oct	Balance b/f	14,992.18

Cutler and Co

Date 2003	Details	Amount £	Date 2003	Details	Amount £
1 Sep	Bank	5,320.01	1 Sep	Balance b/f	10,640.01
30 Sep	Balance c/f	11,641.50	5 Sep	Purchase Day Book	6,321.50
		16,961.51			16,961.51
			1 Oct	Balance b/f	11,641.50

SUBSIDIARY (PURCHASE) LEDGER

Thrower Ltd

Date	Details	Amount	Date	Details	Amount
2003		£	2003		£
19 Sep	Purchase Return	2,284.93	1 Sep	Balance b/f	9,139.74
22 Sep	Bank	6,717.72	9 Sep	Purchase Day Book	1,560.60
22 Sep	Discount received	137.09			
30 Sep	Balance c/f	1,560.60			
		10,700.34			10,700.34
			1 Oct	Balance b/f	1,560.60

Pentagon Glassware

Date	Details	Amount	Date	Details	Amount
2003		£	2003		£
16 Sep	Bank	9,279.10	1 Sep	Balance b/f	12,209.34
16 Sep	Discount received	488.37	1 Sep	Purchase Day Book	8,621.95
30 Sep	Balance c/f	14,599.31	15 Sep	Purchase Day Book	3,535.49
		24,366.78			24,366.78
			1 Oct	Balance b/f	14,599.31

See Task 7 on next page

Your assessor is likely to tell you:

- The receipt of £5,000 represents further capital contributed to the business by Jane Knight.
- The payment of £8,730.50 represents Matthew Denby's personal expenses which were paid directly from the partnership bank account.

PART TWO TASKS

Part Two includes Tasks 7 – 12. You should spend about two hours on this part.

Adjusting and extending the trial balance

Background information

The suspense account has been investigated. It arose as follows:

*   An amount of £5,000 was paid into the firm's bank account in May 2003. The other side of the entry was never made.

*   A cheque for £8,730.50 was paid out of the firm's bank account in December 2002 to an interior design consultant. The shop has not been redecorated since early in 2001 and Anne Thorpe has told you that as far as she knows the partners have no plans to carry out any work of this kind on the shop or the office in the near future. Again, the other side of the entry was never made.

Task 7

*   Describe how you would attempt to discover what the receipt and the payment represented so that you can account for them correctly. Set out your answer on page 194.

    Note: once you have completed your answer you should ask your assessor to explain what these items represented (if your assessor is not available, see the details in the box on the bottom of the previous page).

*   Draft journal entries, dated 30 September 2003, to clear the balance on the suspense account. Set out your entries, with full narrative, on page 195.

Task 8

Details of Delft's closing stocks are given on page 173.

*   Calculate the value of the closing stock of finished goods for resale at 30 September 2003 for inclusion in the trial balance. Use page 196 for your answer.

Task 9

Enter adjustments in the second two columns of the extended trial balance on pages 192 and 193 for the following:

*   the journal entries prepared in Task 7

*   the closing stock calculated in Task 8

*   the accruals and prepayments listed on page 173

Task 10

Extend the trial balance as follows:

*   Total all columns of the trial balance.

*   Make entries to record the net profit or loss for the year ended 30 September 2003.

Drafting final accounts

Background information

The partnership agreement contains the following provisions.

- Interest on capital is to be paid at 5% on the balance at the year end on the capital accounts. No interest is paid on the current accounts.

- The partners are entitled to the following salaries for the year ended 30 September 2003:

  Jane Knight   £5,000

- Profit after deducting interest on capital and salaries is shared between the partners in the following ratio:

  Matthew Denby   4/10

  Amina Iqbal   4/10

  Jane Knight   2/10

Task 11

- Prepare an appropriation account for the partnership for the year ended 30 September 2003. Set out your answer on page 197.

- Prepare the partners' current accounts for the year ended 30 September 2003. Set out your answer on page 198.

Note: you should work to the nearest £.

Task 12

Using the completed extended trial balance on pages 192 and 193 and your answers to Task 11:

- Prepare the profit and loss account of Delft for the year ended 30 September 2003. Set out your answer on page 199.

- Prepare the balance sheet of Delft at 30 September 2003. Set out your answer on page 200.

Note: you should work to the nearest £.

Stock at 30 September 2003

Stocks were counted at close of business on 30 September 2003. Details are summarised below:

	Cost	Estimated selling price
	£	£
China (See Note)	26,879.00	30,542.70
Cutlery	5,613.50	7,129.14
Glassware	3,760.00	2,760.00
	36,252.50	40,431.84

Note: the stock of china includes some Spode Blue Italian crockery which originally cost £5,500.00. This stock should be treated as "seconds" and will be sold for 50% of its cost price.

Accruals and prepayments at 30 September 2003

All calculations are made to the nearest month.

Only two items are expected to give rise to material accruals or prepayments:

Rates

On 1 September 2003, the partnership paid rates of £2,500, covering the three months to 30 November 2004.

Electricity

On 30 July 2003 the partnership paid a bill of £253.25, covering the three months to 30 June 2003. The bill for the following three months has not yet been received.

ANSWER PAGES

Tasks 1, 2 and 3

EXTRACT FROM FIXED ASSET REGISTER

Description/serial no	Date acquired	Original cost £	Depreciation £	NBV £	Funding method	Disposal proceeds £	Disposal date
Motor vehicles							
Delivery van Z754 WIL	1/5/01	10,500.00			Cash		
Year ended 30/9/01			3,500.00	7,000.00			
Year ended 30/9/02			3,500.00	3,500.00			
Delivery van WF02 DAN	5/8/02	11,250.00			Cash		
Year ended 30/9/02			3,750.00	7,500.00			

Tasks 1, 2 and 3, continued

EXTRACT FROM FIXED ASSET REGISTER

Description/serial no	Date acquired	Original cost £	Depreciation £	NBV £	Funding method	Disposal proceeds £	Disposal date
Equipment, fixtures and fittings							
Cash register	5/12/00	1,900.00			Cash		
Year ended 30/9/01			475.00	1,425.00			
Year ended 30/9/02			356.25	1,068.75			
Display tables	5/12/00	5,650.00			Cash		
Year ended 30/9/01			1,412.50	4,237.50			
Year ended 30/9/02			1,059.37	3,178.13			
Built in shelves and cupboards	1/11/01	22,500.00			Cash		
Year ended 30/9/02			5,625.00	16,875.00			

continued on next page

Tasks 1, 2 and 3, continued

EXTRACT FROM FIXED ASSET REGISTER

Description/serial no Equipment, fixtures and fittings	Date acquired	Original cost £	Depreciation £	NBV £	Funding method	Disposal proceeds £	Disposal date
Desktop PC (Dell)	12/3/02	1,210.00			Cash		
Year ended 30/9/02			302.50	907.50			
Laser Printer (Samsung)	12/3/02	450.00			Cash		
Year ended 30/9/02			112.50	337.50			

Tasks 1 and 3

Journal			
Date 2003	Account names and narrative	Dr £	Cr £

Task 2

MEMO
To: From: Subject: Date:

Task 3

Calculation of depreciation charge on shop premises

Tasks 4 and 6

MAIN LEDGER

Administrative expenses

Date 2003	Details	Amount £	Date 2003	Details	Amount £
1 Sep	Balance b/d	19,652.84			
30 Sep	Bank	221.09			

Bank current account

Date 2003	Details	Amount £	Date 2003	Details	Amount £
30 Sep	Receipts	33,155.15	1 Sep	Balance b/d	989.20
			30 Sep	Payments	36,612.83

Capital: Matthew Denby

Date 2003	Details	Amount £	Date 2003	Details	Amount £
			1 Sep	Balance b/d	20,000.00

Tasks 4 and 6, continued

MAIN LEDGER

Capital: Amina Iqbal

Date 2003	Details	Amount £	Date 2003	Details	Amount £
			1 Sep	Balance b/d	20,000.00

Capital: Jane Knight

Date 2003	Details	Amount £	Date 2003	Details	Amount £
			1 Sep	Balance b/d	15,000.00

Current account: Matthew Denby

Date 2003	Details	Amount £	Date 2003	Details	Amount £
30 Sep	Bank	1,000.00	1 Sep	Balance b/d	14,641.40

Tasks 4 and 6, continued

MAIN LEDGER

Current account: Amina Iqbal

Date 2003	Details	Amount £	Date 2003	Details	Amount £
1 Sep	Balance b/d	892.61			
30 Sep	Bank	500.00			

Current account: Jane Knight

Date 2003	Details	Amount £	Date 2003	Details	Amount £
30 Sep	Bank	500.00	1 Sep	Balance b/d	7,321.81

Delivery expenses

Date 2003	Details	Amount £	Date 2003	Details	Amount £
1 Sep	Balance b/d	6,971.86			
30 Sep	Bank	134.85			

Tasks 4 and 6, continued

MAIN LEDGER

Depreciation

Date 2003	Details	Amount £	Date 2003	Details	Amount £

Discounts received

Date 2003	Details	Amount £	Date 2003	Details	Amount £
			1 Sep	Balance b/d	7,001.67
			30 Sep	Purchase ledger control	808.25

Disposals

Date 2003	Details	Amount £	Date 2003	Details	Amount £

Tasks 4 and 6, continued

MAIN LEDGER

Equipment, fixtures and fittings: Cost

Date 2003	Details	Amount £	Date 2003	Details	Amount £
1 Sep	Balance b/d	31,710.00			

Equipment, fixtures and fittings: Accumulated depreciation

Date 2003	Details	Amount £	Date 2003	Details	Amount £
			1 Sep	Balance b/d	9,343.12

Motor vehicles: Cost

Date 2003	Details	Amount £	Date 2003	Details	Amount £
1 Sep	Balance b/d	21,750.00			

Tasks 4 and 6, continued

MAIN LEDGER

Motor vehicles: Accumulated depreciation

Date 2003	Details	Amount £	Date 2003	Details	Amount £
			1 Sep	Balance b/d	10,750.00

Petty cash

Date 2003	Details	Amount £	Date 2003	Details	Amount £
1 Sep	Balance b/d	200.00			

Purchases

Date 2003	Details	Amount £	Date 2003	Details	Amount £
1 Sep	Balance b/d	273,372.25			
30 Sep	Purchase day book	27,869.60			

Tasks 4 and 6, continued

MAIN LEDGER

Purchase ledger control account

Date 2003	Details	Amount £	Date 2003	Details	Amount £
30 Sep	Bank	30,273.78	1 Sep	Balance b/d	45,698.70
30 Sep	Discount received	808.25	30 Sep	Purchase day book	32,746.78

Purchase returns

Date 2003	Details	Amount £	Date 2003	Details	Amount £
			1 Sep	Balance b/d	8,934.89

Rates, light and heat

Date 2003	Details	Amount £	Date 2003	Details	Amount £
1 Sep	Balance b/d	15,059.92			
30 Sep	Bank	2,500.00			

Tasks 4 and 6, continued

MAIN LEDGER

Sales

Date 2003	Details	Amount £	Date 2003	Details	Amount £
			1 Sep	Balance b/d	354,949.35
			30 Sep	Bank	28,217.15

Shop premises: Cost

Date 2003	Details	Amount £	Date 2003	Details	Amount £
1 Sep	Balance b/d	105,000.00			

Shop premises: Accumulated depreciation

Date 2003	Details	Amount £	Date 2003	Details	Amount £
			1 Sep	Balance b/d	4,200.00

Tasks 4 and 6, continued

MAIN LEDGER

Stock

Date 2003	Details	Amount £	Date 2003	Details	Amount £
1 Sep	Balance b/d	28,687.70			

Sundry creditors

Date 2003	Details	Amount £	Date 2003	Details	Amount £

VAT

Date 2003	Details	Amount £	Date 2003	Details	Amount £
30 Sep	Purchase day book	4,877.18	1 Sep	Balance b/d	4,912.63
30 Sep	Bank	62.28	30 Sep	Bank	4,938.00

Tasks 4 and 6, continued

MAIN LEDGER

Wages and salaries

Date 2003	Details	Amount £	Date 2003	Details	Amount £
1 Sep	Balance b/d	16,715.09			
30 Sep	Bank	1,420.83			

Task 5

Purchase ledger account balances at 30 September 2003

	£
Fine Ceramics Ltd	
Cutler and Co	
Thrower Ltd	
Pentagon Glassware	_____
	_____
Purchase ledger control account:	
Balance at 30 September 2003	_____
Difference	_____

Reason for the difference:

Task 5, continued

Journal			
Date	Account names and narrative	Dr	Cr
2003		£	£

Tasks 6, 9 and 10:   **EXTENDED TRIAL BALANCE**

account name	balances per ledger	
	Dr £	Cr £
Administrative expenses		
Bank current account		
Capital: Matthew Denby		
Capital: Amina Iqbal		
Capital: Jane Knight		
Current account: Matthew Denby		
Current account: Amina Iqbal		
Current account: Jane Knight		
Delivery expenses		
Depreciation		
Discounts received		
Disposals		
Equipment, fixtures and fittings: Cost		
Equipment, fixtures and fittings: Depreciation		
Motor vehicles: Cost		
Motor vehicles: Depreciation		
Petty cash		
Purchases		
Purchase ledger control account		
Purchase returns		
Rates, light and heat		
Sales		
Shop premises: Cost		
Shop premises: Depreciation		
Stocks		
Sundry creditors		
VAT		
Wages and salaries		
Total		

name	**DELFT**				date	**30 September 2003**	
adjustments		**profit and loss account**		**balance sheet**			
Dr £	Cr £	Dr £	Cr £	Dr £	Cr £		

Task 7

Task 7, continued

Journal			
Date	Account names and narrative	Dr	Cr
2003		£	£

Task 8

Stock valuation at 30 September 2003

Task 11

Appropriation of profit at 30 September 2003

	£	£
Net profit		
Interest on capital:		
Matthew Denby		
Amina Iqbal		
Jane Knight		
Salaries:		
Jane Knight		
Balance of net profit		
Share of profit:		
Matthew Denby		
Amina Iqbal		
Jane Knight		

Task 11, continued

Partners' current accounts

	Matthew Denby £	Amina Iqbal £	Jane Knight £		Matthew Denby £	Amina Iqbal £	Jane Knight £

Task 12

DELFT

Profit and loss account for the year ended 30 September 2003

	£	£
Sales		
Opening stock		
Purchases		
Closing stock		
Cost of sales		
Gross profit		
Discounts received		
Less expenses:		
Administrative expenses		
Delivery expenses		
Depreciation		
Profit/loss on disposal of fixed assets		
Rates, light and heat		
Wages and salaries		
Net profit for the year		

Task 12, continued

DELFT

Balance sheet at 30 September 2003

	£	£
Fixed assets:		
Shop premises		
Equipment, fixtures and fittings		
Motor vehicles		
Current assets:		
Stock		
Prepayments		
Petty cash		
Current liabilities:		
Bank overdraft		
Trade creditors		
Sundry creditors		
VAT		
Accruals		
Net current liabilities		
Capital accounts:		
Matthew Denby		
Amina Iqbal		
Jane Knight		
Current accounts:		
Matthew Denby		
Amina Iqbal		
Jane Knight		

Unit 5
Maintaining financial records and preparing accounts

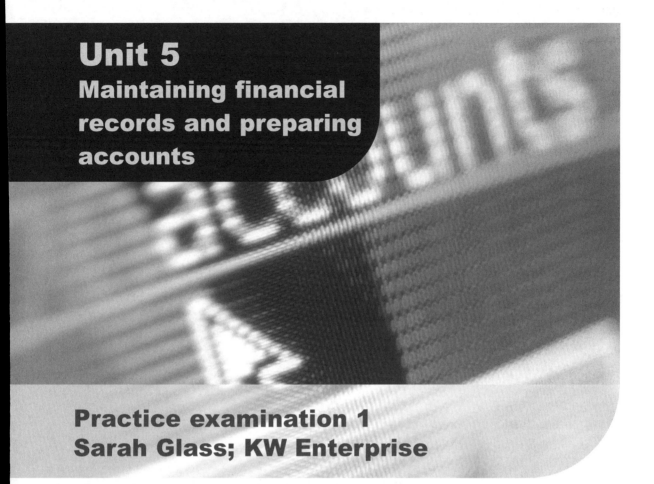

Practice examination 1
Sarah Glass; KW Enterprise

NVQ Element coverage

5.1 maintaining records relating to capital acquisition and disposal

5.2 collecting and collating information for the preparation of final accounts

5.3 preparing the final accounts of sole traders and partnerships

Suggested time allocation

Three hours and fifteen minutes (to include a recommended fifteen minutes reading time).

PRACTICE EXAMINATION 1
SARAH GLASS; KW ENTERPRISE

This Examination is in two sections.

You have to show competence in both sections.

You should therefore attempt and aim to complete every task in both sections.

You should spend about 80 minutes on Section 1 and 100 minutes on Section 2.

SECTION 1

You should spend about 80 minutes on this section.

DATA

Sarah Glass is considering buying a small wholesale business from Hassan Abdul.

Hassan Abdul has provided some financial information for his business, which is set out below and on the next page.

You are an accounting technician at Aggie Accountancy, an accounting firm which is advising Sarah Glass.

Assets and liabilities as at 30 April 2003

	£
Freehold premises at cost	104,000
Less Depreciation to date	20,800
	83,200
Fixtures and fittings at cost	22,750
Less Depreciation to date	13,650
	9,100
Stock	43,160
Debtors	52,300
Prepaid general expenses	700
Cash	1,000
	97,160
Creditors	46,750
Bank overdraft	22,600
	69,350

Summary of the business bank account for the year ended 30 April 2004

2004	£	2004	£
Cash sales	292,180	Opening balance	22,600
Receipts from debtors	722,800	Payments to creditors	789,950
		General expenses	8,110
		Salaries	92,420
		Drawings	36,800
		Closing balance	65,100
	1,014,980		1,014,980

Other information

- The profit margin achieved on all sales was 20%

- The value of the closing stock held on 30 April 2004 is unknown

- Depreciation is calculated as follows:

    Premises – 2% per annum on cost

    Fixtures and fittings – 10% per annum on cost

- All cash is banked at the end of each day, apart from a cash float. During the year, the cash float was decreased from £1,000 to £800

- On 30 April 2004 the outstanding balances were:

	£
Creditors	64,100
Debtors	59,020
Accrual for general expenses	210

Sarah Glass has asked you to calculate some key figures for the year ended 30 April 2004.

Task 1.1

Calculate the total value of the credit sales for the year ended 30 April 2004.

Task 1.2

Calculate the total sales for the year ended 30 April 2004.

Task 1.3

Calculate the total value of the purchases for the year ended 30 April 2004.

Task 1.4

Calculate the value of the closing stock held on 30 April 2004.

Task 1.5

Starting with the gross profit for the year ended 30 April 2004 (calculated in 1.4 above), prepare the profit and loss account for the year ended 30 April 2004. Show clearly the net profit or loss for the year.

Task 1.6

Show the net book value of the fixed assets held on 30 April 2004.

Task 1.7

When Sarah Glass looks at your figures, she does not understand why the closing balance in the bank account is different to the net profit shown in task 1.5.

(a)　　Give TWO examples of transactions that affect the profit figure, but do not affect the bank account.

(b)　　Give ONE example of a transaction that affects the bank account, but does not directly affect the profit figure

DATA

Sarah Glass is considering forming a partnership with her brother who could provide some of the money needed to fund the purchase of the business from Hassan Abdul.

Sarah Glass does not understand how partnerships are shown in accounts. She is worried that the money each partner puts into, and takes out of, the business, will not be shown separately.

Task 1.8

Using the headed paper on the next page, write a memo to Sarah Glass explaining:

- how partner interests are shown in the financial statements of a partnership
- the difference between the types of accounts that exist
- what types of transactions the different accounts would show

MEMO	
To:	Sarah Glass
From:	Accounting Technician
Subject:	Partnership accounts
Date:	Today

SECTION 2

You should spend about 100 minutes on this section.

DATA

Kelly Wainwright is the proprietor of KW Enterprise, a business that buys and sells carpets and other floor coverings.

*   The financial year end is 30 June 2004.

*   You are employed by Kelly Wainwright to assist with the bookkeeping.

*   The business currently operates a manual system consisting of a main (general) ledger, a subsidiary (sales) ledger and a subsidiary (purchases) ledger.

*   Double entry takes place in the main (general) ledger. Individual accounts of debtors and creditors are kept in subsidiary accounts.

*   You use a purchases day book, a sales day book, a purchases returns day book and a sales returns day book. Totals from the various columns of the day books are transferred into the main (general) ledger.

At the end of the financial year on 30 June 2004, the balances were extracted from the main (general) ledger and entered in an extended trial balance as shown on the next page.

It was found that the total of the debit column of the trial balance did not agree with the total of the credit column. The difference was posted to a suspense account.

Task 2.1

Make appropriate entries in the adjustment columns of the extended trial balance on the next page to take account of the following.

(a)   Depreciation needs to be provided as follows:

*   Motor vehicles – 25% per annum reducing balance method

*   Fixtures and fittings – 15% per annum straight line method

(b)   Rent payable is £3,000 per month.

(c)   An invoice relating to goods received by KW Enterprise on 29 June 2004 had not been entered in the accounts. The invoice totalled £2,350 including VAT at 17.5%. The goods have been included in the stock valuation on 30 June 2004.

(d)   Stock was valued at cost on 30 June 2004 at £30,040. This includes £625 which is the cost of a carpet that is dirty and needs cleaning. The cost of cleaning it will be £50, and the carpet can then be sold for £300.

(e)   On reviewing the debtors, Kelly Wainwright decides that £300 should be written off. The provision for doubtful debts should be 4% of the outstanding debtors.

	KW Enterprise			
	Trial balance as at 30 June 2004			
Description	Ledger balance		Adjustments	
	Dr £	Cr £	Dr £	Cr £
Capital		61,280		
Sales		487,360		
Sales returns	8,900			
Purchases	286,330			
Purchases returns		650		
Stock at 1 July 2003	25,870			
Rent	33,000			
General expenses	87,700			
Motor expenses	28,540			
Bad debts	1,220			
Provision for doubtful debts		3,200		
Motor vehicles (M.V.) at cost	36,000			
Provision for depreciation (M.V.)		19,560		
Fixtures and fittings (F&F) at cost	57,020			
Provision for depreciation (F&F)		34,580		
Drawings	30,000			
Sales ledger control account	56,550			
Purchases ledger control account		31,500		
Bank		2,700		
VAT		10,070		
Suspense		230		
Depreciation				
Provision for doubtful debts – adjustment				
Closing stock – P & L				
Closing stock – balance sheet				
Accruals				
Totals	**651,130**	**651,130**		

DATA

You have found the following errors.

(a)   The VAT column of the sales day book had been undercast by £380.

(b)   The net column of the sales day book had been overcast by £870.

(c)   Sales of £5,080 had been transferred from the total column of the sales day book into the sales ledger control account as £5,800.

Task 2.2

Prepare journal entries to correct the errors using the blank journal below.

Dates and narratives are not required.

Note: Do not adjust your answer to task 2.1 (e).

Journal		
	Dr £	Cr £

DATA

On 30 June 2004 the balances of the accounts in the subsidiary (purchases) ledger were listed, totalled and compared with the updated balance in the purchases ledger control account.

The list of balances totalled £33,770. After an investigation, the following errors were found in the list taken from the subsidiary (purchases) ledger.

(a)   A creditor account with a balance of £290 had been omitted from the list.

(b)   A credit purchase of £960 (inclusive of VAT) had been omitted from a creditor's account.

(c)   Purchase returns of £80 (inclusive of VAT) had been omitted from a creditor's account.

(d)   A payment to a creditor of £500 had been credited to the creditor's account.

(e)   A creditor's balance of £780 had been entered in the list as £870.

Task 2.3

Enter the appropriate adjustments in the table below. For each adjustment show clearly the amount involved and whether the amount is to be added or subtracted.

£

Total from purchase ledger   ....

Adjustment for (a)   add / subtract   ....

Adjustment for (b)   add / subtract   ....

Adjustment for (c)   add / subtract   ....

Adjustment for (d)   add / subtract   ....

Adjustment for (e)   add / subtract   ....

Revised total to agree with purchases ledger control account   ....

Task 2.4

Some of the fixtures and fittings used by KW Enterprise were originally purchased on 1 January 2003 for £8,400. Assume these fixtures and fittings were sold on 1 August 2004 for £6,000.

(a)   What would be the net book value of these fixtures and fittings on the date of disposal if the depreciation is calculated on a monthly basis?

£ . . . .

. . . .

(b)   What would be the amount of profit or loss on disposal of the fixtures and fittings?

(Circle the correct answer for profit or loss)

Profit / Loss

£ . . . .

. . . .

Task 2.5

The list of balances on page 209 includes an amount of £10,070 as VAT.

(a)   To whom will KW Enterprise pay this amount?

(b)   Explain how the VAT balance has been arrived at.

DATA

- Kelly Wainwright has looked at the work you have done so far on the accounts.

- She is interested in the reconciliation you did between the subsidiary (purchases) ledger and the purchases ledger control account.

- She does not understand why you did the reconciliation.

Task 2.6

Using the headed paper on the next page, write a brief memo to Kelly Wainwright, explaining:

- the purpose of the subsidiary (purchases) ledger

- whether the subsidiary (purchases) ledger is part of the double-entry accounting system

- the purpose of the purchases ledger control account

- whether the purchases ledger control account is part of the double-entry accounting system

- the reasons for doing the reconciliation

MEMO

To:	Kelly Wainwright
From:	Accounting Technician
Subject:	Reconciliations
Date:	Today

Unit 5
Maintaining financial records and preparing accounts

Practice examination 2
David Nix; ABC Traders

NVQ Element coverage

5.1 maintaining records relating to capital acquisition and disposal

5.2 collecting and collating information for the preparation of final accounts

5.3 preparing the final accounts of sole traders and partnerships

Suggested time allocation

Three hours and fifteen minutes (to include a recommended fifteen minutes reading time).

PRACTICE EXAMINATION 2
DAVID NIX; ABC TRADERS

This Examination is in two sections.

You have to show competence in both sections.

You should therefore attempt and aim to complete every task in both sections.

You should spend about 80 minutes on section 1, and 100 minutes on section 2.

SECTION 1

You should spend about 80 minutes on this section.

DATA

David Nix started trading on 1 June 2003. He opened a shop selling general groceries.

David Nix does not keep a double-entry book-keeping system.

You are an accounting technician at Aggie Accountancy, an accounting firm which is preparing the final accounts for David Nix. You are working on his accounts for the year ended 31 May 2004. David Nix has given you the following information.

A summary of the business bank account for the year ended 31 May 2004

2004	£	2004	£
From cash account	89,750	Payments to trade creditors	59,400
		Wages	8,105
		General expenses	7,550
		Drawings	11,000
Closing balance	1,305	Fixtures	5,000
	91,055		91,055

Other information

•   The cash from sales is banked at the end of the day, except a float of £100 that is kept in the till. During the year, the following cash payments were made from the till, before banking.

                              £

General expenses   2,150

Wages   1,900

•   The value of the stock on 31 May 2004 was unknown, but the profit margin achieved on all sales was 1/3.

•   The fixtures are expected to last for five years, depreciating evenly over time, with no residual value.

•   On 31 May 2004, the outstanding balances were:

                              £

Trade creditors   9,320

General expenses   780

Task 1.1

Prepare the cash account for the year ended 31 May 2004, clearly showing the total sales.

Task 1.2

Calculate the gross profit for the year ended 31 May 2004.

Task 1.3

Calculate the total purchases for the year ended 31 May 2004.

Task 1.4

Calculate the cost of the closing stock for the year ended 31 May 2004.

ADDITIONAL DATA

David Nix tells you that the value of the closing stock, at cost, on 31 May 2004 was £3,650. Also, in February 2004, the shop was broken into and some stock was stolen. He does not know the value of the stolen stock.

Task 1.5

Calculate the cost of the stolen stock.

Task 1.6

Calculate the actual gross profit for the year ended 31 May 2004.

Task 1.7

Starting with the gross profit for the year ended 31 May 2004 (calculated in 1.6, above), prepare David Nix's profit and loss account for the year ended 31 May 2004. Show clearly his net profit or loss for the year.

Task 1.8

David has heard of a profit mark-up, but does not understand the difference between profit margin and profit mark up.

Explain the difference between profit margin and profit mark-up.

DATA

David Nix needs to buy some more fixtures, but cannot afford to pay for them out of the bank account. He has heard about leasing and hire purchase of fixed assets, and needs to know more about these methods of financing.

Task 1.9

Using the headed paper on the next page, write a memo to David Nix explaining:

- the terms leasing and hire purchase;

- the difference between the two methods of financing.

	MEMO
To:	David Nix
From:	Accounting Technician
Subject:	Leasing and hire purchase
Date:	Today

SECTION 2

You should spend about 100 minutes on this section.

DATA

Andrea and Brian Colvin are the owners of ABC Traders, a business that buys and sells garden furniture.

*   The financial year end is 30 June 2004.

*   The business uses an integrated computerised accounting system consisting of a main ledger, a purchases ledger and a stock ledger.

*   There are no credit customers.

*   You work for Aggie Accountancy, an accounting firm which prepares final accounts for Andrea and Brian Colvin.

At the end of the financial year on 30 June 2004, the trial balance shown on the next page was taken from the computer system.

	Dr £	Cr £
Accruals		5,500
Advertising	8,740	
Bank	51,809	
Capital account – Andrea		35,000
Capital account – Brian		40,000
Cash in hand	550	
Closing stock – trading account		58,450
Closing stock – balance sheet	58,450	
Computer equipment at cost	12,900	
Computer equipment accumulated depreciation		7,460
Current account – Andrea		9,045
Current account – Brian	3,750	
Drawings – Andrea	25,240	
Drawings – Brian	19,610	
Fixtures and fittings at cost	48,140	
Fixtures and fittings accumulated depreciation		17,890
General expenses	82,440	
Opening stock	69,375	
Prepayments	3,500	
Purchases	476,725	
Purchases ledger control		45,320
Rent	18,200	
Sales		762,918
VAT		13,500
Wages	115,654	
Total	995,083	995,083

DATA

After checking the trial balance, you discover

- some year-end adjustments that need to be made
- some errors that need correcting

(a)   Depreciation needs to be provided as follows:

- fixtures and fittings – 10% per annum straight line method
- computer equipment – 25% per annum reducing balance method

(b)   General expenses include insurance of £2,400, which was paid for the year ending 31 December 2004.

(c)   £2,000 is owed in wages on 30 June 2004.

(d)   An invoice of £1,250 for advertising has been debited to purchases account.

(e)   A journal entry for general expenses accrued of £400 relating to June 2004 has been entered into the accounting system as:

Debit   Accruals   £400

Credit General expenses   £400

(f)   The closing stock valuation in the trial balance is taken from the computerised accounting system at cost price. Some items were reduced in price after the financial year end. The details are as follows:

Stock code	Quantity in stock 30 June 2004	Cost £	Normal selling price £	Reduced selling price £
FRO	50	25.00	45.00	30.00
TKT	20	80.00	150.00	75.00
WHE	12	20.00	30.00	10.00

Task 2.1

Prepare journal entries to record the above adjustments and correct the errors.

Dates and narratives are not required. Use the blank journal provided on the next page. There is space for your workings below the journal.

JOURNAL		
	Dr £	Cr £

Workings

Task 2.2

Prepare a profit and loss account for the partnership for the year ended 30 June 2004, showing clearly the gross profit and the net profit. Use the trial balance from page 223 and your journal adjustments from page 225.

ADDITIONAL DATA

The partnership agreement allows for the following:

Partners' salaries

- Andrea   £12,000
- Brian   £10,000

Interest on capital

        5% per annum on the balance at the year end

Profit share

- Andrea   one-half
- Brian   one-half

Task 2.3

Prepare the appropriation account for the partnership for the year ended 30 June 2004.

Task 2.4

Update the current accounts for the partnership for the year ended 30 June 2004. Show clearly the balances carried down.

CURRENT ACCOUNTS

2003		Andrea £	Brian £	2003		Andrea £	Brian £
1 Jul	Balance b/d		3,750	1 Jul	Balance b/d	9,045	

Task 2.5

Prepare a balance sheet for the partnership as at 30 June 2004, showing clearly the total net assets. Use the trial balance from page 223 and your journal adjustments from page 225.

ADDITIONAL DATA

From 1 July 2004, the partners agree to change the profit share to

* Andrea two-thirds
* Brian one-third

It is agreed that goodwill should be valued at £30,000. No goodwill is to remain in the accounts following the change.

Task 2.6

(a) Update the capital accounts for the partnership as at 1 July 2004 in order to reflect the change in profit share. Show clearly the balances carried down.

CAPITAL ACCOUNTS

2004		Andrea £	Brian £	2004		Andrea £	Brian £
				1 Jul	Balances b/d	35,000	40,000

(b) On reviewing her capital account following changes to the profit share, Andrea wants to know why her capital account balance has altered.

Draft a brief note to Andrea Colvin explaining

* why the adjustment to her capital account was necessary
* how the adjustment has affected her capital in the business

Note to Andrea Colvin

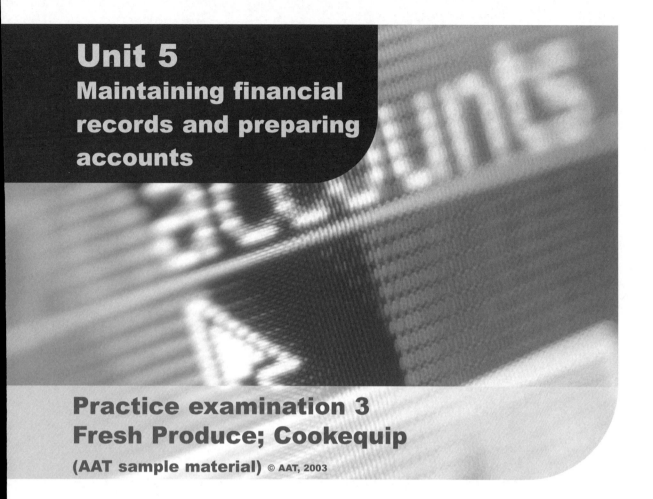

Unit 5
Maintaining financial records and preparing accounts

Practice examination 3
Fresh Produce; Cookequip
(AAT sample material) © AAT, 2003

NVQ Element coverage

5.1   maintaining records relating to capital acquisition and disposal

5.2   collecting and collating information for the preparation of final accounts

5.3   preparing the final accounts of sole traders and partnerships

Suggested time allocation

Three hours and fifteen minutes (to include a recommended fifteen minutes reading time).

PRACTICE EXAMINATION 3
FRESH PRODUCE; COOKEQUIP

This Examination is in two sections.

You have to show competence in both sections.

You should therefore attempt and aim to complete every task in both sections.

You should spend about 80 minutes on Section 1 and 100 minutes on Section 2.

SECTION 1

You should spend about 80 minutes on this section.

DATA

Tony Bond owns Fresh Produce, a business that buys and sells fruit and vegetables. All sales are on credit terms.

Tony Bond does not keep a double entry bookkeeping system.

You are an accounting technician at A1 Accountancy, an accounting firm which prepares the final accounts for Fresh Produce. You are working on the accounts for Fresh Produce for the year ending 31 December 2004. Your colleague has already summarised the cash and bank accounts, which are shown below.

Fresh Produce			
Bank account summary for the year ended 31 December 2004			
	£		£
Receipts from debtors	868,760	Opening balance	9,380
Closing balance	4,985	Purchases	661,300
		Vehicle running expenses	9,065
		Purchase of replacement vehicle	7,500
		Wages	42,500
		Drawings	25,500
		Cash	118,500
	873,745		873,745

Fresh Produce

Cash account summary for the year ended 31 December 2004

	£		£
Opening balance	3,500	Purchases	118,700
Bank	118,500	Closing balance	3,300
	122,000		122,000

The balance sheet from last year is also available:

Fresh Produce

Balance sheet as at 31 December 2003

	£	£	£
	Cost	Accumulated Depreciation	Net Book Value
Fixed assets			
Vehicles	23,025	12,750	10,275
Current assets			
Trade debtors		152,360	
Prepayment		1,535	
Cash		3,500	
		157,395	
Current liabilities			
Bank overdraft		9,380	
Net current assets			148,015
Total net assets			158,290
Capital account			158,290

Other information

•   Tony Bond gives unsold stock to a charity at the end of each day, so there are no stocks.

•   The prepayment was for vehicle insurance.

•   The total owed by debtors on 31 December 2004 was £148,600.

•   There are no trade creditors.

•   During the year Tony Bond part-exchanged one of the vehicles. The vehicle originally cost £8,000 in 2001. He was given a part-exchange allowance of £2,000 against a replacement vehicle.

•   The depreciation policy is 25% per annum reducing balance. A full year's depreciation is applied in the year of acquisition and none in the year of disposal.

•   Vehicle insurance of £1,200 was paid in October 2004 for the twelve months to September 2005.

Task 1.1

Prepare the sales ledger control account for the year ended 31 December 2004, showing clearly the total sales.

Dr   **Sales Ledger Control Account**   Cr

2004		£	2004		£

Task 1.2

Calculate the total purchases for the year ended 31 December 2004.

Task 1.3

Calculate the net book value of the vehicle that was part-exchanged during the year.

Task 1.4

Prepare the disposals account for the year ending 31 December 2004.

Dr   **Disposals Account**   Cr

2004		£	2004		£

Task 1.5

(a)   Calculate the cost of the replacement vehicle purchased during the year ending 31 December 2004.

(b)   Calculate the revised total vehicle cost as at 31 December 2004.

(c)   Calculate the depreciation charge for the year ending 31 December 2004.

(d)   Calculate the updated accumulated depreciation as at 31 December 2004.

Task 1.6

(a)   Calculate the adjustment necessary as at 31 December 2004 for the vehicle insurance paid in October 2004, stating clearly whether it is a prepayment or an accrual.

(b)   Calculate the adjusted vehicle running expenses for the year ended 31 December 2004.

(c)   Name the accounting concept, referred to in FRS18, which supports the adjustment you have made to vehicle running expenses.

Task 1.7

Prepare a trial balance as at 31 December 2004, taking into account your answers to the above tasks, and all the other information you have been given.

FRESH PRODUCE
TRIAL BALANCE AS AT 31 DECEMBER 2004

Name of account	Dr £	Cr £
....	....	....
....	....	....
....	....	....
....	....	....
....	....	....
....	....	....
....	....	....
....	....	....
....	....	....
....	....	....
....	....	....
....	....	....
....	....	....
....	....	....
....	....	....
Total	....	....

Task 1.8

You see a note in the file stating that Tony Bond normally marks up all his purchases by 15%. Your supervisor suggests that you check your sales figures in Task 1.1 by using this information.

(a)   Using your purchases figure from Task 1.2 and the normal mark-up of 15%, recalculate the sales for the year ending 31 December 2004.

(b)   Calculate the difference between the figure you have calculated in 1.8(a), and your answer to Task 1.1.

(c)   Draft a memo to your supervisor, Maisie Bell. In your memo:

•   state the discrepancy you have found in preparing the sales figure for Fresh Produce, referring to your answer to Task 1.8(b)

•   offer a possible explanation for the discrepancy

•   ask Maisie Bell what she would like you to do about the discrepancy

Use the memo format on the next page.

MEMO		
To:	Maisie Bell	
From:	Accounting Technician	
Subject:	Fresh Produce discrepancy	
Date:	15 January 2005	

SECTION 2

You should spend about 100 minutes on this section.

DATA

David Arthur and Liz Stanton are the owners of Cookequip, a shop selling cookery equipment to the public.

- The financial year end is 31 December 2004.
- The business uses an integrated computerised accounting system consisting of a main ledger, a purchase ledger and a stock ledger.
- There are no credit customers.
- You work for a firm of chartered accountants who prepare final accounts for David Arthur and Liz Stanton.

At the end of the financial year on 31st December 2004, the following trial balance was taken from the computer system:

	Dr £	Cr £
Accruals		5,500
Advertising	10,893	
Bank	11,983	
Capital account – Liz		30,000
Capital account – David		10,000
Cash in hand	500	
Closing stock – trading account		28,491
Closing stock – balance sheet	28,491	
Computer equipment at cost	15,000	
Computer equipment accumulated depreciation		3,750
Consultancy fees	3,800	
Current account – Liz		6,750
Current account – David	3,500	
Drawings – Liz	5,000	
Drawings – David	16,250	
Fixtures and fittings at cost	90,000	
Fixtures and fittings accumulated depreciation		53,000
Office expenses	4,000	
Opening stock	25,834	
Prepayments	5,000	
Purchases	287,532	
Purchases ledger control		14,811
Rent	23,000	
Sales		465,382
VAT control		11,453
Wages	98,354	
Total	629,137	629,137

Task 2.1

After checking the trial balance, you discover

- some year-end adjustments that need to be made
- some errors that need correcting

Prepare journal entries to record the following adjustments and correct the errors. Dates and narratives are not required. Use the blank journal provided on the next page. There is space for your workings below the journal.

(a)   Depreciation needs to be provided as follows:

- Fixtures and fittings – 20% per annum reducing balance method
- Computer equipment – 25% per annum straight line method

(b)   The closing stock valuation in the trial balance is taken from the computerised system at cost, but some items were reduced in price after the year end. The details are shown below:

Stock Code	Quantity in stock 31 December 2004	Cost £	Normal selling price £	Reduced selling price £
AB625	150	7.00	8.00	4.00
AD184	2	180.00	220.00	150.00
BS552	4	6.00	10.25	7.50

(c)   Accountancy fees of £1,500 need to be accrued.

(d)   A journal entry for prepaid rent of £1,500 relating to January 2005 has been posted as follows:

Dr   Rent   £1,500

Cr   Prepayments   £1,500

(e)   An invoice for £500 for consultancy fees has been debited to the purchases account.

JOURNAL		
	Dr £	Cr £

Workings

Task 2.2

Prepare a profit and loss account for the partnership for the year ended 31 December 2004, showing clearly the gross profit and the net profit. Use the trial balance from page 241 and your journal adjustments from page 243.

ADDITIONAL DATA

- The partnership agreement allows for the following:

  Partners' salaries

  – Liz   £8,000

  – David   £12,000

  Interest on capital

  – 2.5% per annum on the balance at the year end

  Profit share, effective until 30 June 2004

  – Liz   two thirds

  – David   one third

  Profit share, effective from 1 July 2004

  – Liz   one half

  – David   one half

- No accounting entries for goodwill are required.

- Profit accrued evenly during the year

Task 2.3

Prepare the appropriation account for the partnership for the year ended 31 December 2004.

Task 2.4

Update the current accounts for the partnership for the year ended 31 December 2004. Show clearly the balances carried down.

CURRENT ACCOUNTS

2004		Liz £	David £	2004		Liz £	David £
1 Jan	Balance b/d		3,500	1 Jan	Balance b/d	6,750	

Task 2.5

On reviewing the accounts, Liz Stanton asked a question about the partners' current accounts. She wanted to know why the balances brought down for the two partners were on opposite sides.

Draft a note to Liz Stanton explaining:

(a)   what the balance on a partner's current account represents

(b)   what a debit balance on a partner's current account means

(c)   what a credit balance on a partner's current account means

Note to Liz Stanton

DATA

On reviewing the accounts, David Arthur wants to know why you adjusted the stock valuation from the computer system and how this affected the profit you calculated.

Task 2.6

Draft a note to David Arthur explaining:

(a)   why the adjustment was necessary, naming the relevant accounting standard

(b)   how your adjustment affected the profit

Note to David Arthur

Page for workings

Appendix:
photocopiable resources

These pages may be photocopied for student use, but remain the copyright of the author. It is recommended that they are enlarged to A4 size.

These pages are also available for download from the Resources Section of www.osbornebooks.co.uk

The forms and formats include:

■   ledger accounts   page 250

■   journal page   page 251

■   extended trial balance   page 252

■   fixed asset register   page 253

■   trading and profit and loss account   page 254

■   balance sheet   page 255

■   memorandum   page 256

Dr   Cr

Date	Details	Amount	Date	Details	Amount
		£			£

Dr   Cr

Date	Details	Amount	Date	Details	Amount
		£			£

Dr   Cr

Date	Details	Amount	Date	Details	Amount
		£			£

JOURNAL

Details	Dr £	Cr £

EXTENDED TRIAL BALANCE

Account name	Ledger balances Dr £	Ledger balances Cr £	Adjustments Dr £	Adjustments Cr £	Profit and loss Dr £	Profit and loss Cr £	Balance sheet Dr £	Balance sheet Cr £
Closing stock: Profit and loss								
Closing stock: Balance sheet								
Accruals								
Prepayments								
Depreciation								
Bad debts								
Provision for doubtful debts:adjustment								
Net profit/loss								

name..................   date..................

FIXED ASSET REGISTER PAGE

EXTRACT FROM FIXED ASSET REGISTER

Description/serial no	Date acquired	Original cost £	Depreciation £	NBV £	Funding method	Disposal proceeds £	Disposal date

SOLE TRADER: TRADING AND PROFIT AND LOSS ACCOUNT

This example layout for final accounts is for sole trader businesses; for partnerships, the layout will need to be adjusted to take note of the partners' capital and current accounts).

	£	£	£	
TRADING AND PROFIT AND LOSS ACCOUNT OF .... **(name)**				
FOR THE YEAR/PERIOD ENDED ....**(date)**				
Sales			......	
Less Sales returns			......	
Net sales			......	(a)
Opening stock		......		
Purchases	......			
Carriage in	......			
Less Purchases returns	......			
Net purchases		......		
		......		
Less Closing stock		......		
Cost of sales			......	(b)
Gross profit (a) – (b)			......	(c)
Add other income, eg				
Discount received			......	
Provision for doubtful debts (reduction)			......	(d)
Profit on sale of fixed assets			......	
Other income			......	
(c) + (d)			......	(e)
Less overheads, eg				
Vehicle running expenses		......		
Rent		......		
Rates		......		
Heating and lighting		......		
Telephone		......		
Salaries and wages		......		
Discount allowed		......		
Carriage out		......		
Depreciation		......		
Loss on sale of fixed assets		......		
Bad debts written off		......		
Provision for doubtful debts (increase)		......		
			......	(f)
Net profit (e) – (f)			......	(g)

SOLE TRADER: BALANCE SHEET

BALANCE SHEET OF .... (name) AS AT .... (date)

Fixed assets	£ Cost (a)	£ Prov for dep'n (b)	£ Net (a) – (b)	
Intangible: Goodwill	......	......	......	
Tangible: Premises	......	......	......	
Equipment	......	......	......	
Vehicles	......	......	......	
etc	......	......	......	
	......	......	......	(c)

Current assets
Stock (closing)   ......
Debtors   ......
Less provision for doubtful debts   ......
       ......
Prepayments   ......
Bank   ......
Cash   ......
      ......   (d)

Less Current liabilities
Creditors   ......
Accruals   ......
Bank overdraft   ......
      ......   (e)

Working capital (or **Net current assets**) (d) – (e)   ...... (f)
(c) + (f)   ...... (g)
Less Long-term liabilities
Loans   ...... (h)
NET ASSETS (g) – (h)   ...... (i)

FINANCED BY
Capital
Opening capital   ......
Add net profit (from profit and loss account)   ......
      ......
Less drawings   ......
      ...... (i)

Note: balance sheet balances at points (i)

Practical point: When preparing handwritten final accounts it is usual practice to underline all the headings and sub-headings shown in bold print in the example layout.

MEMORANDUM

To:

From:

Subject:

Date: